P9-DNV-043

DISCARDED
FROM
UNH LIBRARY

Enzymic Catalysis

MODERN PERSPECTIVES IN BIOLOGY

Under the Editorship of

HARLYN O. HALVORSON *The University of Wisconsin*
MOLECULAR BIOLOGY

HERSCHEL L. ROMAN *University of Washington*
GENETICS

EUGENE BELL *Massachusetts Institute of Technology*
DEVELOPMENTAL BIOLOGY

Published:

A HISTORY OF GENETICS
A. H. Sturtevant CALIFORNIA INSTITUTE OF TECHNOLOGY

MOLECULAR ORGANIZATION AND BIOLOGICAL FUNCTION
John M. Allen, Editor THE UNIVERSITY OF MICHIGAN

BIOSYNTHESIS OF SMALL MOLECULES
Georges N. Cohen CENTRE NATIONAL DE LA RECHERCHE SCIENTIFIQUE,
  GIF-SUR-YVETTE, FRANCE

THE GENETIC CODE: The Molecular Basis for Genetic Expression
Carl. R. Woese UNIVERSITY OF ILLINOIS

THE PRIMARY STRUCTURE OF PROTEINS: Principles and Practices
  for the Determination of Amino Acid Sequence
Walter A. Schroeder CALIFORNIA INSTITUTE OF TECHNOLOGY

EPISOMES
Allan M. Campbell STANFORD UNIVERSITY

ENZYMIC CATALYSIS
John Westley THE UNIVERSITY OF CHICAGO

UNH LIBRARY
3 4600 00421 8043

John Westley

Professor of Biochemistry
The University of Chicago

ENZYMIC
CATALYSIS

HARPER & ROW, PUBLISHERS, NEW YORK, EVANSTON, AND LONDON

Chem
QD
501
.W623
c. 2

ENZYMIC CATALYSIS
Copyright © 1969 by John Westley

Printed in the United States of America. All rights reserved. No
part of this book may be used or reproduced in any manner whatso-
ever without written permission except in the case of brief quotations
embodied in critical articles and reviews. For information address
Harper & Row, Publishers, Incorporated, 49 East 33rd Street,
New York, N.Y. 10016.

Library of Congress Catalog Card Number: 69-13749

CONTENTS

PREFACE

This book is conceived primarily as an aid to graduate students in biochemistry and allied fields who combine a curiosity about enzyme mechanisms with some background in organic chemistry and biochemistry, and at least an introduction to physical chemistry. There are currently available both detailed treatments of the physical organic chemistry of reaction mechanisms that may be applicable to enzymes and some excellent detailed treatments of enzyme kinetics. Nonetheless, for the nonspecialist in enzyme mechanisms generally, it appears desirable to have a concise, current account of enzymic catalysis from a phenomenological point of view. The present book is an effort to present this material with as good a balance of the various experimental approaches as the author can manage and a firm resolve to separate the demonstrated from the speculative.

The author hopes (but does not expect) to be forgiven his choice of examples. Comprehensiveness was neither possible nor desirable in a book of this size written for this purpose. The examples used represent a minimum sampling of research to illustrate the principles involved. They were selected pragmatically as material that the author has found useful in helping students to develop an understanding of modern enzymology. Obviously, a large body of fine work has had to go unmentioned.

References to a few good books and reviews dealing with the appropriate subject matter in a more extended treatment or from a different point of view are given at the end of each chapter. Specific references to research reports from which information has been used are also included there. The numbers in parenthesis throughout the text refer to these specific references.

Included in an Appendix are a number of problems that the author

vii

has found useful in engaging the attention of students. Particularly in the uses of kinetic arguments, it appears that involvement with such specific material is an important means to improved understanding.

The author wishes to express his deep appreciation to V. Bloomfield, W. W. Cleland, D. E. Koshland, Jr., and H. R. Levy for skilled critiques of the manuscript and many excellent suggestions.

JOHN WESTLEY

CONVENTIONS

One of the most unfortunate features of enzymology has been the tendency of each author to devise and use his own system of conventional symbols. Such problems are normally solved by international agreement and perhaps, in time, this one will be so dispatched. Up to the present time, however, reform at that level has been inadequate, perpetuating the use of S and P to designate substrate and product, for example, and thereby ignoring sulfur enzymes and phosphoenzymes that are *not* enzyme-substrate or enzyme-product complexes in the sense in which those terms are generally used.

The symbols used in this book have been selected primarily with an eye to avoiding confusion. Capital letters are used to designate substrates and products, excluding, however, the atomic symbols for elements common in biological systems. Where distinction between substrates and products is important, the former are chosen from letters early in the alphabet, the latter from those toward the end. Equilibrium constants are K, rate constants k with a subscript $+$ or $-$ number designating the reaction and its direction. In mathematical equations, concentrations are designated simply by the symbols for the reaction components, the usual brackets being omitted to reduce clutter, since no confusion arises from such usage. In referring to molecular addition complexes, a parenthetical notation has been used. Thus, in mathematical equations, (EA) refers to the concentration of a complex of A with E, whereas EA means "the product of the concentrations of E and A." Some of these usages, e.g., the manner of depicting rate constants, are in accord with the recommendations of the International Union of Biochemistry on enzyme nomenclature. In designating individual enzymes, however, the common trivial names have been used, rather than the catalogued systematic nomenclature.

In writing mechanisms, a "flow" notation similar to that introduced by Baldwin has been used as it reduces redundancies and permits uninterrupted visualization of the progress of substrates through the reaction. At the same time it emphasizes the cyclic role of the enzyme in catalysis. With this type of diagram, reversible reactions are most conveniently indicated by double-headed arrows. That practice has been followed here, where the context of use should ensure the absence of confusion with the symbol often used to indicate resonance. Reactions are numbered in the sequence designated as the positive direction. Finally, the customary thermodynamic and chemical symbols have been employed. Each symbol is defined where it is first used and the entire collection, with definitions, is also presented on pages xi–xiii.

LIST OF SYMBOLS

$A, B, C, \ldots$	substrate, concentration of substrate
A_0	substrate concentration at zero time
(AQ)	combined form of substrate with modifier
ΔC	very small displacement from equilibrium concentration
D	dielectric constant
e	the base of natural logarithms
$\mathbf{e}$	the charge of the electron
E	uncombined enzyme, concentration of uncombined enzyme
$\mathbf{E}$	Arrhenius activation energy
E_0	enzyme concentration at zero time, i.e., total concentration of all forms of enzyme
(EA)	enzyme-substrate complex, concentration of the complex
$(EA)_0$	hypothetical steady-state concentration of (EA) at zero time
ΔE°	standard change in internal energy
(EQ)	enzyme-modifier complex, concentration of the complex
(EAQ)	enzyme-substrate-modifier complex, concentration of the complex
E_p, E_q, E_r	enzymes in a coupled system
ER	substituted enzyme
(ERB)	complex of substituted enzyme with a substrate
e.u.	entropy units, cal mole^{-1} degree^{-1}

ΔG° standard change in free energy

$\Delta G^{\ddagger}$ free energy of activation

h Planck's constant

H hydronium ion concentration

ΔH° standard change in enthalpy

$\Delta H^{\ddagger}$ enthalpy of activation

I inhibited

k rate constant, subscripts refer to numbered reactions; $+$ and $-$ subscripts refer to reaction direction

k' apparent rate constant

$\mathbf{K}$ the Boltzmann constant

$K_a, K_1, \ldots$ equilibrium (association) constant for reaction a, reaction 1, etc.

K_m Michaelis constant; superscript letter designates substrate

K_m^{app} apparent Michaelis constant, inverse negative abscissal intercept of double reciprocal plot

K_Q equilibrium (association) constant for modifier; subscript numbers refer to reaction sites.

K_s equilibrium (dissociation) constant for enzyme-substrate complex

μ ionic strength

N normal, uninhibited

P, Q, R   enzyme-substrate complexes of enzymes E_p, E_q E_r in a coupled system

pK negative logarithm of dissociation constant

pK_m negative logarithm of Michaelis constant

$p\Delta V^{\circ}$ pressure times standard change in volume

Q modifier, concentration of modifier

r radius of approach of charge centers in bimolecular ionic reaction

R the gas constant

$\mathbf{R}$ rate of isotope exchange

$\mathbf{R}_{max}$ maximum rate of isotope exchange

ρ Hammett reaction constant

ΔS° standard entropy change

$\Delta S^{\ddagger}$ entropy of activation; subscripts es and nes refer to the electrostatic and nonelectrostatic contributions, respectively

σ Hammett substituent constant

t time

T absolute temperature

τ relaxation time

v_0 initial velocity

V^{app} apparent maximum velocity, inverse ordinate intercept of double reciprocal plot

V maximum velocity

$X, Y, \ldots$ product, concentration of product

$Z_A, Z_B, \ldots$ ionic charge

INTRODUCTION

The properties of enzymes are compounded of catalyst properties and protein properties. Like other catalysts, enzymes lower the free energies of activation of the reactions they catalyze. Like at least some other catalysts, they show a "saturation effect," i.e., the catalyzed reactions have rates independent of reactant concentrations when those concentrations are sufficiently high. Unlike most other catalysts, however, enzymes have pH and temperature dependence properties that are typical of proteins. Plots of enzyme activity against pH show, in part, inflections at the pK' values of the ionizable groups of proteins, and the thermal stability of enzyme activity is characteristically that of protein tertiary structure.

There are two further properties of enzymes that demonstrate some noteworthy consequences of using proteins as catalysts. These are the remarkably high efficiency of catalysis and the extraordinary substrate specificity of which enzymes are capable, quite surpassing other known catalysts in both of these regards. It is toward the full documentation and ultimately, one hopes, to the full understanding of these two features of enzyme action that much modern research is directed. Just as the foregoing facts have often been stressed by enzymologists, so has it been noted that we do not in fact have complete chemical explanations of these features for even one enzyme. Nevertheless, some strong advances have been made and sufficiently incisive analytical tools may now be available to permit really full elucidation of a few enzyme mechanisms in the near future.

There are in the literature at the present time three different types of studies that seem to be contributing to progress toward this goal. The study of protein chemistry as such is clearly essential to developing an understanding of the mechanisms by which proteins catalyze

1

reactions. We need exhaustive information regarding the interactions of the functional groups available in protein structure, both their interactions with each other and those with other molecules. Another clear prerequisite to the full understanding of enzymic catalysis is the study of catalytic mechanisms as such, the physical organic chemistry of catalysis. In principle the crossroads where these two types of studies meet should yield enzyme mechanisms. That is, once we know both the repertoire of possible interactions available with proteins, and the repertoire of possible catalytic mechanisms, we should have a solid basis on which to proceed. A third, somewhat different approach, however, should certainly turn out to be useful in guiding the conclusions to be drawn. This approach takes the point of view that an understanding of catalysis by enzymes may best be gained by studying reactions catalyzed by enzymes. This is a phenomenological point of view that encompasses two principal types of research: the kinetics of enzyme-catalyzed reactions and the isolation and study of particular enzymes and especially of enzymic intermediates in the catalytic reaction cycle. Most studies of enzyme mechanisms have included elements from all of these approaches, nevertheless retaining a primary orientation toward one of them.

The chapters that follow deal to some extent with all of the above types of studies, as any serious effort to consider enzyme mechanisms must, but unequal space is accorded the different approaches. The student is presumed to have some background in protein chemistry, and only a few aspects which seem especially pertinent to enzymic catalysis are summarized here as a convenient reminder. The physical organic chemistry of catalysis, although not the central topic, also occurs early in the book, in accounts of the general theories of enzyme action. It is the phenomenological approach, however, that is presented in greatest detail, as this is the source of the facts which the eventual elucidation of enzymic catalysis must explain.

PART I

FUNDAMENTALS OF ENZYMOLOGY

Enzymes are protein catalysts. Accordingly, the eventual elucidation of detailed enzyme mechanisms will surely demand an understanding of both the chemistry of proteins and the behavior of catalyzed reactions.

1

THE CHEMISTRY
OF ENZYMES

Enzymes, like all proteins, are composed of α-amino acid residues joined by peptide bonds. The linear sequence of residues in the peptide chain is referred to as the primary structure of protein. The term secondary structure refers to the coiling or folding of the peptide chain that is stabilized by hydrogen bonds between the carbonyl and amido groups of the peptide bonds. Tertiary structure results from further folding that is stabilized by several kinds of interactions between the various amino acid side chains. Finally, quaternary structure is the name given to the association of separate peptide chains into larger aggregates. In addition to the peptide chain, which comprises the bulk of the molecule, a protein may contain another covalently bound chemical grouping referred to as a prosthetic group.

PRIMARY STRUCTURE

The "backbone" of primary structure is a series of peptide bonds, similar for all proteins. The only "backbone" differences among proteins result from the occurrence of residues of proline and hydroxyproline, which are secondary rather than primary amines. With this exception, the specific features in which proteins differ are consequences of the numbers and locations of the different amino acid side chains in the molecule. The repertoire of interactions in which a particular enzyme may participate, whether these be interactions with substrate molecules and prosthetic groups or intramolecular interactions resulting in tertiary structure of the enzyme itself, is clearly dependent on the chemical properties of these side chains.

Table 1 is a list of the names and structures of the residues common-ly found in proteins. They may be discussed in terms of the groupings indicated there.

The neutral aliphatic residues having no functional groups are unreactive in the usual sense but are capable of van der Waals inter-actions with other molecules or other residues in close spatial proximity. In addition, there may be interactions of nonpolar groups based on mutual repulsion by the aqueous solvent, sometimes referred to as

TABLE 1.   *The Amino Acids Present in Protein Structure*[a]

Neutral aliphatics:

Glycine $^-$OOC—CH$_2$ Valine $^-$OOC—CHCH(CH$_3$)$_2$
                 | |
              $^+$NH$_3$ $^+$NH$_3$

Alanine $^-$OOC—CHCH$_3$ Leucine $^-$OOC—CHCH$_2$CH(CH$_3$)$_2$
                   | |
                $^+$NH$_3$ $^+$NH$_3$

Serine $^-$OOC—CHCH$_2$OH   CH$_3$
                  | |
               $^+$NH$_3$ Isoleucine $^-$OOC—CH—CHCH$_2$CH$_3$
                                                           |
                                                        $^+$NH$_3$

                              OH
                              |
Threonine $^-$OOC—CHCHCH$_3$
                        |
                     $^+$NH$_3$

Acidics:

Aspartic acid $^-$OOC—CHCH$_2$COOH   Glutamic $^-$OOC—CHCH$_2$CH$_2$COOH
                           | acid |
                        $^+$NH$_3$ $^+$NH$_3$

Basics:

Lysine $^-$OOC—CH(CH$_2$)$_3$CH$_2$$^+NH_3$ Histidine $^-$OOC—CHCH$_2$— HC—N
                   | | ‖   ‖
                NH$_2$ $^+$NH$_3$ C   CH
                                                                         N
                                                                         H

                                              NH$_2$
                                             ⁄
Arginine $^-$OOC—CH(CH$_2$)$_3$NHC   +
                   | ⟍
                NH$_2$ NH$_2$

Sulfur-containing:

Cysteine $^-$OOC—CHCH$_2$SH   Methionine $^-$OOC—CH(CH$_2$)$_2$SCH$_3$
                     | |
                  $^+$NH$_3$ $^+$NH$_3$

TABLE 1. (*Continued*)

Aromatics:

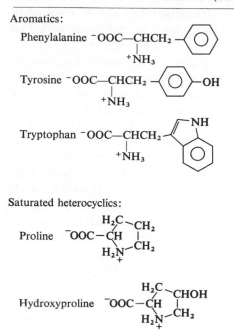

Saturated heterocyclics:

---

^a The ionic forms indicated are the predominant forms present in solutions of the free amino acids in pure water.

hydrophobic bonding. The glycine residue appears to have some special properties occasioned by the absence of any side chain. In particular, this residue permits sharper turning of the peptide chain in its folded conformation.

The aliphatic residues containing hydroxyl groups possess somewhat more specific reactivity. The aliphatic hydroxyl group can be a donor in hydrogen bond formation. Moreover, as will be discussed in detail in Chap. 6, some serine hydroxyl groups in some enzymes have quite remarkable activity as nucleophilic agents.

The acidic residues bear single negative charges at physiological pH values. Accordingly, they may be involved in ionic interactions. These residues are responsible for the negative contribution to the net charge of the protein molecule. They also may be involved in several ways in hydrogen bond formation. The unionized carboxyl group is a good hydrogen donor and the carboxylate ion is a good acceptor. Furthermore, the amides of these carboxylate groups, which are the glutaminyl and asparaginyl residues of proteins, can participate in hydrogen bonding in much the same way as the peptide bond groups of the protein backbone. Carboxylate groups may also be involved in the chelation complex binding of metal ions that are firmly bound to some proteins.

The basic residues are cationic in their protonated forms. Accordingly, they are involved in charge interactions and contribute the positive component to the net charge of the protein molecule. The guanidinium group of arginine may have a special role in forming stable ion pairs with carboxylates in nonpolar regions of the structure. The ε-amino group of lysyl residues can react with carbonyl compounds, eliminating water reversibly to form Schiff bases. In addition, the protonated nitrogen atoms can serve as donors and the deprotonated forms as acceptors in hydrogen bond formation, although only histidine imidazole nitrogen can be important in the latter role in the physiological pH range. The weakly basic imidazole ring also has further properties that have given it a central role in discussions of possible enzyme mechanisms. In its unprotonated form it contains two nitrogen atoms with clearly distinguishable properties, one electrophilic and one nucleophilic. Protonation of the imidazole results in a loss of the nucleophilic activity. Since the pH for this protonation is in the physiological range and since even free imidazole displays some striking catalytic properties in neutral solutions, much of the work on enzyme models has dealt with imidazole derivatives. Imidazoles are also powerful ligands for the formation of coordination complexes of transition metal ions. It is possible, too, that the imidazole ring serves as an acceptor in charge-transfer interactions with the indole ring of tryptophan or with electron donors not present in the primary structure of protein.

The sulfur-containing residues are important because of the special chemical properties of sulfur. The great polarizability of the sulfur atom makes it especially effective both as an entering group and as a leaving group in nucleophilic substitution. The thiol group of cysteine is an excellent nucleophile and even the thioether of methionine has nucleophilic properties, as evidenced by the formation of sulfonium derivatives like S-adenosylmethionine. Cysteine very readily undergoes a reversible oxidation to cystine, in which form it supplies the only fully covalent bonds that occur between different peptide chains or nonadjacent residues of the same chain. These disulfide bonds under some conditions can participate in disulfide interchange reactions in which the residues attached to the sulfur atoms are switched: $RSSR + R'SSR' \rightleftharpoons 2RSSR'$. Like carboxylate and imidazole groups, sulfur-containing groups may also form coordination complexes with metal ions. The sulfur-containing residues are probably not importantly involved in side-chain hydrogen bonding.

The aromatic residues constitute a rather heterogeneous category including those amino acids containing benzene rings.[1] All of these residues are capable of strong van der Waals interactions and are strongly hydrophobic. The phenolic tyrosyl structure can, in addition, participate as a donor in hydrogen bonding. The indole ring of tryptophan has some interesting and distinctive properties. It is the only protein residue capable of entering very readily into charge transfer interactions as a donor. Indoles are excellent electron donors for the formation of charge transfer complexes with pyridinium compounds and other electrophilic structures. Furthermore, tryptophyl residues are responsible for practically all of the ultraviolet fluorescence of proteins. This statement is true even of proteins containing much tyrosine and little tryptophan, although tyrosyl (and, to a lesser extent, phenylalanyl) residues contribute to the ultraviolet absorbance of proteins. Both the ultraviolet absorbance and the fluorescence yield of a tryptophyl residue are highly sensitive to its intimate environment in the protein. In addition, the pyrrole nitrogen of tryptophan may be a donor in some hydrogen bond interactions.

Finally, the saturated heterocyclic prolyl and hydroxyprolyl residues are of importance for their stereochemical properties. Formation of peptide bonds with these cyclic secondary α-amino acids results in more rigid structures than is the case where only the primary α-amino acids are involved. The limited occurrence of hydroxyproline, only in proteins of connective tissue, and the exclusive occurrence of the single isomer having the hydroxyl and carboxyl groups in the trans configuration, suggests that the hydroxyl group of this residue serves a special structural role.

SECONDARY STRUCTURE

The conformation of a polypeptide in solution depends in part on the direct interactions of the peptide groups with each other. The highly regular, "crystalline" structure of synthetic polypeptides, in contrast to the amorphous or random coil structures of many other polymers, has suggested that there is a "natural" conformation for polypeptides in general. Careful assessment of bond lengths and bond angles based on the dimensions found for the planar peptide bonds

---

[1] Although the imidazole ring of histidine is also an aromatic structure, it is most usefully classified with the basic amino acids as above.

existing in crystals of small peptides has placed important restrictions on the possible models for this conformation. The additional assumptions that every peptide carbonyl group and every peptide amido group must be involved in hydrogen bonding and that the rotation around each single bond must be restricted to a conformation having potential rotational energy near the minimum level, have further narrowed the choices. The result for peptides bonded intramolecularly has been a right-handed helical model having 3.6 residues per turn (1). The existence of helical structures having the predicted dimensions in synthetic polypeptides has been confirmed by studies using a variety of physical methods, including X-ray crystallography. This α-helix, as it is designated, in which each peptide group is hydrogen bonded to the third peptide group beyond, is regarded as the most probable model for sections of the backbone structure of the globular proteins, the class to which the enzymes belong. It is stressed, however, that the total conformation of a globular protein will be modified from the simple regularity of the α-helix by the presence of disulfide bonds, of prolyl residues, which interrupt the helical arrangement and cause changes in its direction, and of the side-chain interactions responsible for tertiary structure. In fact, the high resolution structures thus far obtained for enzymes by the X-ray crystallographers (2–8) do not contain large amounts of α-helix. There are some helical segments but these are interspersed both with less regular structure and with a second type of regular structure, the extended " pleated sheet" once thought limited to the insoluble fibrous proteins.

TERTIARY STRUCTURE

Both the hydrodynamic properties of proteins in solution and the unit cell dimensions obtained from their single-crystal X-ray diffraction patterns indicate that the molecules are compact and rigid. These features exist in a degree much greater than can be accounted for by helical secondary structure alone, even when the prolyl residues and disulfide bonds are taken into consideration. The ease with which this compactness can often be disrupted also suggests that it is not stabilized by covalent bonds. It is the interactions of the residue side chains, on the basis of their chemical properties indicated above, that stabilize these closely folded tertiary structures of globular proteins. The forces involved are individually weak: ionic interactions, hydrogen bonding, hydrophobic bonding, and van der Waals forces. The cooperative occurrence of many such interactions throughout the folded structure is what gives it sufficient stability to exist at ordinary temperatures. It has been very difficult to assess the relative extents to which these different types of interactions are actually involved in tertiary structure and in fact there is no general agreement on this point.

The twisted, folded model for enzyme molecules that emerges from all of these considerations appears somewhat chaotic—except that all molecules having the same primary structure are twisted and folded in the same way. This common conformation shared by the molecules of any particular protein, although it is only one of many possible for that polypeptide, is nonetheless determined by the primary structure. Stabilization of the particular tertiary structure present occurs by specific interactions between specific residues as they occur in the sequence; e.g., certain carboxylate groups are hydrogen bonded with certain tyrosyl residues, certain carboxylate groups interact electrostatically with certain arginyl guanidinium groups, and certain nonpolar groupings of various residues are maintained in close contact by mutual repulsion by the solvent. In general, alterations of amino acid composition or sequence would cause changes in these interactions and thus could give rise to different conformations. Folding into the particular conformation in which the protein molecules occur probably happens sequentially, a short section at a time, during protein synthesis, as the residues of each newly formed molecule are released in the same sequence from the messenger ribonucleic acid template.

It should be noted that the existence of secondary and tertiary structure results in many differences between the properties of the enzyme molecule and the algebraic sum of the corresponding properties of its component residues. Some differences in hydrodynamic and other physical properties are qualitatively predictable on the basis of relatively gross information regarding the molecular sizes and shapes involved. In addition, a number of finer differences demand our attention as they must be of importance in the catalytic role of enzymes.

Each enzyme molecule in solution bears a net charge, significant in its interactions with other macromolecules, which is not exactly predictable from a knowledge of its primary structure. Of greater importance for its interactions with the small molecular substrates are the localized charges of both signs at different sites on the surface of the enzyme. There may also be fairly extensive regions consisting largely of nonpolar, hydrophobic side chains and donor or acceptor areas for either hydrogen bonding or charge transfer complex formation. Again, however, the chemical effects of these localized factors could not be predicted from a knowledge of either primary structure or the hydrodynamic properties of the enzyme molecules. This situation arises from two important features of globular protein structure: (a) the existence of an effective "surface" and "interior" of the molecule and (b) the juxtaposition in the folded structure of groups remote in the primary sequence.

Protein crystals, like protein solutions, contain a quantity of water. Even in crystals, however, this water is found to be external to the macromolecular structure itself. There is a substantial molecular interior which is essentially out of contact with the aqueous solvent and is inaccessible to even small molecular solutes. A further consequence of the existence of an inaccessible interior has to do with the stability of the folded structure. The interior of the molecule may have a physical chemical environment in which hydrogen bonding, hydrophobic bonding, and indeed all of the types of interactions thought to be important in stabilizing secondary and tertiary structure can be more stable than would be possible in simple aqueous solution.

One consequence of this fact is that many side-chain groups may be "masked" or "buried" in the interior of the molecule and thus not titratable or otherwise detectable with the usual chemical reagents. Some alteration may also be expected in physical properties like ultraviolet absorption and fluorescence which depend on properties of the residue side chains. Only when the protein molecule has been entirely unfolded (at extremes of pH, at high temperatures, in the presence of detergents, or in high concentrations of urea or guanidine) do the total properties of the side-chain groups approximate those expected from the amino acid composition.

The effects of tertiary structure in juxtaposing groups remote in the primary sequence must be of great importance in enzymic catalysis. In particular the active site region of an enzyme (i.e., that area at which the substrates attach and are reacted) is made up of residues that are not adjacent in linear sequence but are brought close together by the folding of structure. Specific examples illustrating this point will be detailed in a subsequent chapter, but it should be clear from general considerations that, for example, high local concentrations of certain residues on the enzyme surface could result in regions capable of polyfunctional, and therefore relatively strong, hydrogen bonding. Similarly, there may be regions having relatively high affinities for nonpolar groups, and so on. Moreover, the spatial array of side-chain groups may be involved in determining substrate specificity, where different types of groups in the substrate must interact with the enzyme in a fixed spatial relationship. Finally, the folding of enzyme structure presents the possibility of a cooperative effect of a different sort, in which interaction of the substrate with one enzyme group facilitates its attack by a second, strategically placed group. All of these possibilities seem evident in the detailed X-ray crystallographic structures for enzymes thus far available and must receive attention in our efforts to explain the catalytic properties of enzymes.

QUATERNARY STRUCTURE

The association of polypeptide chains into larger aggregates has been called quaternary structure. The forces involved are evidently the same as in tertiary structure, where they result in intramolecular rather than intermolecular linking. Such association of protein subunits apparently occurs very widely. In several instances it is known to be of importance in enzymic activity, as it is in the oxygen binding function of hemoglobin, but the detailed basis for these effects is not yet well understood. In general terms, however, the cause of such associations may be said to be the increased micellar stability that results from covering exposed hydrophobic areas of the molecule. Thus two molecules of a protein that has insufficient hydrophilic residues to form a complete hydrophilic surface layer around the hydrophobic interior will be more stable in aqueous solution associated as a dimer with apposed hydrophobic regions.

COENZYMES AND PROSTHETIC GROUPS

The functioning of many enzymes requires the presence of small amounts of chemical species other than the L-amino acids that make up the bulk of protein structure. These may be metal ions or organic residues (sometimes also containing metal ions) called cofactors.[2] Chemically, the cofactors are exceedingly various, and they fulfill a corresponding variety of functions in enzymic catalysis. Most of the nutritionally essential trace elements and water-soluble compounds that are vitamins for one organism or another have been shown to function in cofactor forms.

A distinction is made between two types of cofactors, termed coenzymes and prosthetic groups. These have customarily been defined on the basis of the ease with which the cofactor-enzyme combination

[2] It is usual to distinguish categorically between metal ions and the organic cofactors, but on a functional basis it is difficult to see why the cyclic oxidation-reduction of the copper ions in ascorbate oxidase, for example, should be classified separately from the cyclic oxidation-reduction of the flavin in succinate dehydrogenase.

could be disrupted. As Dixon and Webb (9) have pointed out, however, the distinction on this basis is not extremely useful since, although some prosthetic groups are attached to enzymes by covalent bonds, some are evidently not. Furthermore, the equilibrium position in the reversible binding of some coenzymes to some enzymes is very far in the direction of combination. In fact, there is a complete spectrum of "binding constants" and only at the extremes do they afford a clear-cut basis for classification.

For this reason, Dixon and Webb have suggested a functional basis for the prosthetic group–coenzyme distinction. Prosthetic groups are those groups which may complete their catalytic reaction cycles attached to the same enzyme; coenzymes are those which require two different enzymes in the course of their catalytic cycles. This is, of course, another way of saying that a prosthetic group is a part of the enzyme structure, while a coenzyme is simply a substrate with a special, cyclic function. Accordingly, the functional definition is not at odds with the earlier ideas on this topic, but it does hold the promise of providing easier and clearer application. It is the definition used throughout this book.

The evident function of a cofactor is to provide a specific chemical property not easily attained with the amino acid residues alone. In some cases this is understood in detail; in others it is not. A metal ion, for example, could serve simply by providing a strong cationic site for attachment of an anionic substrate. Alternatively, or in addition, the metal ion bound to the enzyme may undergo a cyclic oxidation-reduction process; i.e., it may function as an electron carrier, as the copper in ascorbate oxidase or the iron porphyrin in the cytochromes. Among the organic cofactors, both nicotinamide-adenine dinucleotide (NAD) and the flavins clearly function as oxidation-reduction carriers. Many of the other cofactors (e.g., biotin, the purine ribotides, coenzyme A, etc.) function as group transfer carriers. Lipoate has both a group transfer and an oxidation-reduction role, as does folic acid, in a somewhat different sense. Pyridoxal phosphate, while not directly involved as either an oxidation-reduction or group transfer carrier, is nonetheless intimately involved in catalysis, having a direct role in the bond-breaking steps of many reactions. Thiamine pyrophosphate, too, in its action as a cofactor is evidently directly involved in attack on the substrate molecule, although it combines this function with a group carrier role as well.

These reasonably well-established functions of cofactors, whether coenzymes or prosthetic groups, are examples that should be very instructive. There seems little reason to doubt that the catalytic participation of definite individual amino acid side-chain groups can be dealt with in much the same terms.

GENERAL REFERENCES

Scheraga, H. A.: *Protein Structure*, Academic, New York, 1961.

Tanford, C.: *Physical Chemistry of Macromolecules*, Wiley, New York, 1961.

Boyer, P. D., H. Lardy, and K. Myrbäck (eds.): *The Enzymes*, 2nd ed., Vol. 1, Academic, New York, 1959. Chapter 10 by K. V. Linderstrøm-Lang and J. A. Schellman.

Hirs, C. H. W.: *Methods Enzymol.* 11, 1967.

Steiner, R. F.: *The Chemical Foundations of Molecular Biology*, Van Nostrand, New York, 1965.

Neurath, H. (ed.): *The Proteins*, 2nd ed., Academic, New York, 1963. Especially the chapters by H. A. Scheraga in Vol. I and J. H. Schellman and C. Schellman in Vol. II.

Bernhard, S. A.: *The Structure and Function of Enzymes*, Benjamin, New York, 1968.

SPECIFIC REFERENCES

1. Pauling, L., and R. B. Corey: *Proc. Natl. Acad. Sci. U.S.*, **37**: 241 (1951).
2. Blake, C. C., D. F. Koenig, G. A. Mair, A. C. T. North, D. C. Phillips, and V. R. Sarma: *Nature*, **206**: 757 (1965).
3. Kartha, G., J. Bello, and D. Harker: *Nature*, **213**: 862 (1967).
4. Avey, H. P., M. O. Boles, C. H. Carlisle, S. A. Evans, S. J. Morris, R. A. Palmer, B. A. Woolhouse, and S. Shall: *Nature*, **213**: 557 (1967).
5. Wyckoff, H. W., K. D. Hardman, N. M. Allewell, T. Inagami, D. Tsernoglou, L. N. Johnson, and F. M. Richards: *J. Biol. Chem.*, **242**: 3749 (1967).
6. Reeke, G. R., J. A. Hartsuck, M. L. Ludwig, F. A. Quiocho, T. A. Steitz, and W. N. Lipscomb: *Proc. Natl. Acad. Sci. U.S.*, **58**: 2220 (1967).
7. Fridborg, K., K. K. Lilja, J. Lundin, B. Strandberg, R. Strandberg, B. Tilander, and G. Wiren: *J. Mol. Biol.*, **25**: 505 (1967).
8. Mathews, B. W., P. B. Sigler, R. Henderson, and D. M. Blow: *Nature*, **214**: 652 (1967).
9. Dixon, M. and E. C. Webb: *Enzymes*, 2nd ed., Academic, New York, 1964, p. 450.

2

THE VELOCITIES
OF ENZYME-CATALYZED
REACTIONS

In the direct study of enzymic catalysis, we are usually limited to observation of the overall catalyzed reaction. What can ordinarily be measured is the concentration of a substrate or of a product in the reaction mixture at various times. Such measurements, which constitute the determination of reaction velocity (ideally of instantaneous velocity), can be made under a great variety of experimental conditions to yield information about the catalyzed reaction. This descriptive information is the raw material of enzyme kinetics. Any proposed catalytic mechanism must be in accord with the kinetic data. A principal use of enzyme kinetic data, then, is in eliminating otherwise possible mechanistic schemes that do not accurately describe the catalysis under study. For this reason it has sometimes been remarked that kinetic data cannot really prove anything; they can only disprove things. It should be noted that this "failing" is true quite generally of evidence relating to mechanisms. An experimental observation is either consistent with or not consistent with a proposed mechanism. In the former case it "proves" nothing; in the latter case it definitely disproves the proposed mechanism.[1] Recent efforts (1,2) to formulate kinetic possibilities exhaustively, however, hold real promise that for many mechanisms it will be possible kinetically to eliminate with finality all but one of the reasonable possibilities. As we shall see in later chapters, this has in fact proved to be possible in at least some cases.

---

[1] Perhaps we should use "prove" in its original sense of "test" (as in "the exception that proves the rule"); then kinetic data could always "prove" mechanisms.

EMPIRICAL OBSERVATIONS OF CATALYZED REACTIONS

The study of reaction kinetics is not very old. Chemical kinetics can be traced back only a little more than a century, enzyme kinetics about half that. The fruitful study of chemical kinetics if often dated from 1850, when Wilhelmy reported a kinetic study of the acid-catalyzed hydrolysis of sucrose (3); similarly, enzyme kinetics may be dated from 1902, when A. J. Brown reported a kinetic study of the enzyme-catalyzed hydrolysis of sucrose (4). Brief discussions of sucrose hydrolysis under these two conditions may serve to refresh our memories of kinetic principles and to emphasize the character of enzymic catalysis.

The overall reaction under discussion is

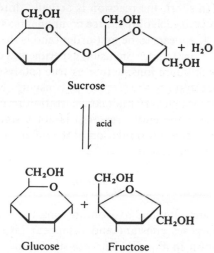

Wilhelmy found that the rate at which the sucrose concentration decreased in an acid solution was directly proportional to that sucrose concentration at any time. In modern terms, we would say that the hydrolysis is first order with respect to sucrose. Mathematically, where A is the sucrose concentration and t the time,

$$-\frac{dA}{dt} = k'A \qquad (1)$$

In the integrated form

$$\frac{A}{A_0} = e^{-k't} \qquad \text{or} \qquad \ln\left(\frac{A_0}{A}\right) = k't$$

where A_0 is the sucrose concentration at zero time and k' is a proportionality constant known as the apparent rate constant. These equations, showing the exponential decrease of sucrose concentration with time (in other words, the linear time dependence of the logarithm of concentration), fairly describe Wilhelmy's experimental results.

Two further factors need to be noted, however. One is the occurrence of water in the stoichiometric equation describing the reaction. The other is the stated acid catalysis of this hydrolysis. Although there is no hydronium ion term in the stoichiometric equation and the time course of the reaction observed by Wilhelmy shows only dependence on sucrose concentration (i.e., it appears to be a simple first-order reaction overall), both of the above factors must also be involved. In fact, Wilhelmy found that the observed rate constant varied with the acidity of the solution. It can also be shown by the use of other solvents that the observed rate constant for hydrolysis varies with the water concentration. In short, the reaction is actually third order, being first order with respect to each of the three components: sucrose, hydronium ion, and water. It appears to be first order (and is therefore said to have a pseudoorder of one) under the usual experimental conditions, for two reasons. The hydronium ions, acting as true catalysts, are not used up and their concentration thus remains constant. Moreover, because water is present in such very high concentration relative to the sucrose, its decrease during the entire reaction is not a significant decrement. Thus, although a correct formulation of the differential kinetic equation is the third-order expression.

$$-\frac{dA}{dt} = kABC \tag{2}$$

where B and C are water and hydronium ions, the last two terms are for all practical purposes constant and disappear into the apparent rate constant k' shown in Eq. (1). The constant k of (2) is the true rate constant for the reaction; its value is independent of all concentrations in the reaction mixture.

One further kinetic concept will be found useful here: molecularity. We have seen that the overall stoichiometry of the reaction, while essential to our understanding, does not necessarily indicate all the participants. We have also found that relatively superficial kinetic observation does not necessarily provide a complete picture of the reaction either. We will not be surprised then to find that even a complete analysis of the overall kinetics cannot provide complete evidence for formulating a detailed mechanism. Thus the third-order dependency of acid-catalyzed sucrose hydrolysis might be an expression of the necessity for each of the three reactants to be involved in the activated complex which decomposes to release glucose and fructose and regenerate a hydronium ion. This would be a termolecular reaction. However, it might equally well in principle be an expression of the occurrence of sequential bimolecular reactions to yield the same overall result. Molecularity, then, is a theoretical concept used to describe a detailed mechanism, specifying the number of molecules involved in the transition state, while order is empirical and relatively gross.

It should also be mentioned that, whereas molecularity obviously must deal in integral numbers, order may have *any* value zero or greater. There are also many reactions which just do not display a simple dependence on concentration of the type expressed as order. These reactions, including enzyme-catalyzed reactions, have no orders but may display approximate pseudoorders under some restricted experimental conditions.

The enzyme-catalyzed hydrolysis of sucrose was found to differ sharply from the acid-catalyzed reaction. In his classic report of 1902, A. J. Brown showed that the absolute amount of sucrose hydrolyzed per unit time in the enzyme-catalyzed reaction was independent of the initial concentration of sucrose in the reaction system (4). In other words, the hydrolysis appeared to be zero order with respect to sucrose. Brown's interpretation of this observation has provided the basis for practically all subsequent thinking regarding the ways in which enzymes operate. He suggested that the enzyme combined with the sucrose and that this complex subsequently decomposed to yield the products and the free enzyme. For such a system containing a small amount of enzyme and a lot of sucrose, Brown's experimental observation would be the expected result. The formal mechanism of the reaction might be indicated in this way:

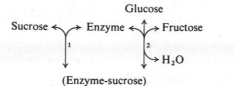

(3)

In such a system the enzyme would cycle continuously. At a sufficiently high concentration of sucrose reaction 1 would be rapid enough to keep the enzyme almost entirely in the enzyme-sucrose form. That is, if reaction 1 were made fast enough reaction 2 would be the rate-limiting step and no further increase in velocity of the overall reaction could be obtained by increasing the sucrose concentration. On the basis of such considerations, Brown predicted, and then demonstrated experimentally, that at sufficiently low sucrose concentrations the behavior of this system would be different. Specifically, there is a region of sucrose concentration in which almost all of the enzyme is in the free form at any time. Under these conditions reaction 1 has a major effect on the overall rate which must then approach proportionality to the sucrose concentration. In other words, at sufficiently low sucrose concentration the enzyme-catalyzed hydrolysis of sucrose has a pseudo-order of approximately one with respect to sucrose.

A great deal of credit must be accorded A. J. Brown for this clear-cut proposal of the existence of an enzyme-substrate complex and his lucid statement of its kinetic consequences. The basic idea was implicit in the work of earlier investigators, as Brown acknowledged, but it was his work that first set forth squarely and then brilliantly illuminated this central concept in enzymic catalysis.

In the year following the appearance of Brown's work, Victor Henri reported the derivation of equations that describe the time course of enzyme-catalyzed reactions in which both the decrease of substrate concentration and the increase of product concentration are taken into account as factors effecting changes in velocity (5). A form of the Henri equation dealing only with the changes in substrate concentration is

$$\frac{X}{t} = V + \frac{K_m}{t} \ln \left(\frac{A_0 - X}{A_0} \right) \tag{4}$$

where A_0 is the substrate concentration at zero time, X is the concentration of substrate that has reacted to form products, V is the theoretical limiting velocity attainable at infinite substrate concentration, and K_m is a constant characteristic of the enzyme and the reaction system. This equation demands that a plot of X/t against $1/t \ln[(A_0 - X)/A_0]$ must yield a straight line (Fig. 1) having a slope equal to K_m, and an ordinate intercept equal to V. A plot of this kind for any reaction provides a test of the applicability of the Henri equation. It should be noted, however, as Henri also showed, that an enzymic reaction in which the enzyme is progressively inhibited by the accumulating reaction products follows a course indistinguishable from a "normal," uninhibited system by this criterion. The plot is of the same form; only the meanings of the constants determined differ.

Because of the occurrence of inhibition by products and further, because of possible partial denaturation of the enzyme during the prolonged course of a reaction, it is usually advantageous to evaluate kinetic behavior on the basis of initial rates. From determinations of substrate or product concentration during the early part of the reaction, the instantaneous velocity of the reaction at zero time may be estimated (Fig. 2). This value should then accurately reflect the reaction rate under

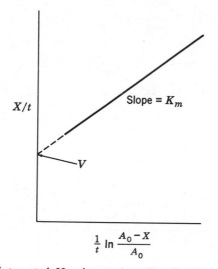

FIG. 1.   Plot of integrated Henri equation (Eq. 4). X, product concentration; A_0, initial substrate concentration; t, time; K_m and V, constants of the reaction system.

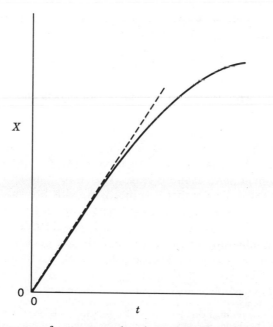

FIG. 2.   Time course of enzyme-catalyzed reaction. The solid line shows the accumulation of product with time. The slope of the dashed line is the initial velocity, v_0.

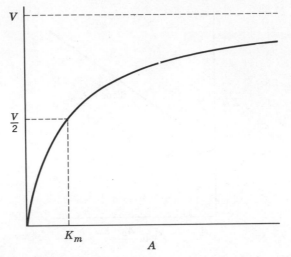

FIG. 3. Plot of Henri equation (Eq. 5). v_0, initial velocity; A, substrate concentration. Note that v_0 does not approach V to greater than 90 percent until A is more than nine times K_m.

known conditions of enzyme and substrate concentration and zero product concentration. When such values are obtained for a series of reaction mixtures in which only the initial substrate concentration (A_0) is varied, a true reflection of the dependence of velocity on substrate concentration is obtained. A differentiated form of the Henri equation suitable for such purposes in describing this dependence is

$$-\frac{dA}{dt} = \frac{dX}{dt} = \text{initial velocity } v_0 = \frac{VA_0}{K_m + A_0} \tag{5}$$

When this equation is written in the form $(V - v_0)(K_m + A_0) = VK_m$, it can be seen to describe a rectangular hyperbola that approaches V and $-K_m$ as limits (Fig. 3). Two facts about this geometry should be noted. One is that it is in accord with Brown's findings, the velocity dependence approximating pseudo first order at low substrate concentrations and pseudo zero order at high substrate concentrations. The second important fact is that nearly all enzyme-catalyzed reactions have been found to display kinetic behavior of this form.[2]

---

[2] The hyperbolic form has certain practical consequences as well. In particular, assay systems, designed for quantitative measurement of the enzyme content of a preparation, usually contain high concentrations of substrates. This practice permits the assay values obtained to be unaffected by small errors made in pipetting the substrate solutions or by the chance presence of variable quantities of certain types of enzyme inhibitors. In fact, however, the initial velocity of the reaction is directly proportional to the enzyme concentration at any concentration of substrate except in the extreme situation where the molar concentrations of substrate and enzyme are of the same order of magnitude.

DERIVATION OF ENZYME KINETIC EQUATIONS FROM SIMPLE MODELS

Implicit in every formal reaction mechanism is a kinetic behavior. Derivation of the kinetic equations that describe this behavior quantitatively makes possible a comparison of the properties of the proposed mechanism with those observed experimentally for the reaction under study. In chemical kinetics the process of derivation usually involves three steps. (a) Equations are written down expressing the interdependencies in the changes of concentration of all reactants, intermediates, and products and stating all of the forms in which each of these entities occurs in the proposed model. This is a matter of translating the mechanism into mathematical terms. (b) Among these equations will be one (or more) involving the overall reaction rate. This differential rate equation is transformed by mathematical manipulation into a form expressing the overall rate in terms of the concentrations of chemical forms that can be measured experimentally. (c) The resulting equation is integrated to obtain an expression for the concentrations of the reactants and products at various times. This is a desirable procedure in general since the primary data obtainable for the actual system with which the model is to be compared are in these terms. It will be recalled, however, that with enzyme kinetic data in particular, the problems of product inhibition and enzyme instability have usually made it necessary to rely on the differential expression directly, employing initial rates obtained in a series of systems at different initial substrate concentrations. For this reason the integration step of the derivation processes is not always carried out.

The complexity encountered in deriving these necessary equations reflects to some extent the complexity of the mechanism involved. For the simple unimolecular reaction, as we have seen, there is only one differential equation to be written, $-(dA/dt) = kA$, and this requires no manipulation. It is already in a form directly testable by experiment. Even the integration of this equation to obtain the exponential or logarithmic form, while convenient, is not really essential for testing.

In contrast, the simplest possible model for an enzyme-catalyzed reaction leads to complexities so great that no rigorous general solution can be obtained. In other words, translation of even the simplest reasonable mechanism into a testable equation requires the use of further simplifying assumptions. The choice of the best assumptions for this purpose has been a source of major difficulty in the kinetic approach to enzyme mechanisms.

To illustrate what is involved, consider the following simple mechanism:

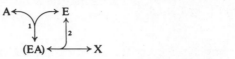

$$(6)$$

where E is the enzyme, A and X are the substrate and product and (EA) is the enzyme-substrate complex. The double-headed arrows indicate reversibility and the reactions are numbered in the sequence to be considered the positive direction. Clearly, this model is simply a generalization of Brown's proposal for the enzyme-catalyzed hydrolysis of sucrose, and as such it should be a reasonably realistic elemental model.[3]

Consider how the concentration of the reaction components indicated in Eq. (6) will vary with time. For the moment make two simplifying assumptions: that the overall reaction is irreversible and that the reactions are to be initiated by mixing equimolar quantities of A and E. Two cases may then be envisioned. Case I: the rate of reaction 1 is very much smaller than the rate of reaction 2, and case II: the rate of reaction 1 is at least comparable to the rate of reaction 2.

The results for cases I and II are shown schematically in Fig. 4. The time course of A concentration is the same for both cases. Also in both cases, E and (EA) necessarily mirror each other. The differences occur in the concentration level attained by (EA) and the existence of a significant lag in the rise of X concentration in case II. In both cases the first occurrence on mixing E and A is the formation of some (EA). In case I, however, (EA) cannot accumulate to a significant extent and the course of X mirrors that of A. In case II some (EA) accumulates, to an extent depending on the actual relationship between the rate constants of reactions 1 and 2, and the maximal velocity of X formation is delayed during a time known as the transient phase.

If the simplifying assumption that E and A must be mixed in equimolar amounts is now abandoned, consider what would happen in a real experiment where the initial concentration of substrate (A_0) would be much greater than that of enzyme (E_0). The picture would be that of Fig. 5. E_0 is very small on this scale; the concentration of (EA) cannot be larger than E_0 for any case. The transient phase is not

---

[3] It is recognized that there are few enzymic reactions that do not involve two substrates, but the one-substrate reaction is still a valuable model. Equations derived from it are often directly applicable to the more complex cases under realizable experimental conditions such as the presence of a constant concentration of the second substrate. The kinetics of two-substrate reactions are considered in Chap. 9.

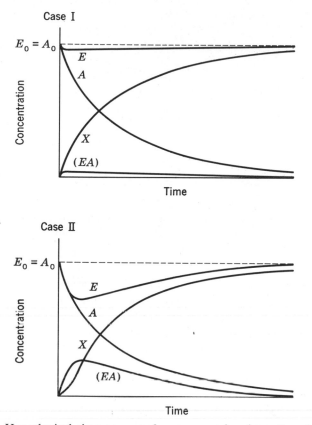

FIG. 4. Hypothetical time course of enzyme-catalyzed reaction. The symbols used refer to Eq. (6). The initial molar concentrations of enzyme and substrate are presumed to be the same.

detectable in the course of X concentration. In short, unless extremely elaborate instrumentation is employed to detect the transient phase, both case I and case II for this situation will look like case I considered above. The changes in E and (EA) concentrations will simply not be significant on a scale appropriate for observation of the changes in substrate and product concentrations.

Finally, abandon the remaining simplifying assumption that the overall reaction is irreversible. Then A will approach some value other than zero and X some value other than A_0. All the rest of the foregoing considerations, however, will hold. Moreover, the problem of overall reversibility can be avoided experimentally by dealing with initial rates. That is, attention would be focused on the earliest part of the reaction,

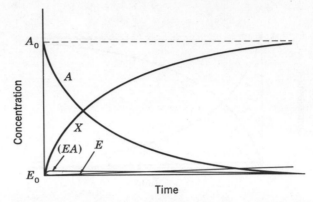

FIG. 5. Time course of enzyme-catalyzed reaction with substrate concentraction much larger than enzyme concentration. The symbols used are as in Fig. 4.

before X accumulates, so that reaction 2 is practically irreversible. Experimentally, initial rate data would be obtained at various substrate concentrations and compared with the differential rather than the integrated kinetic equation for the model.

What these considerations add up to, then, is the opportunity to consider the model on the basis of the behavior shown for case I, without making simplifying assumptions that go beyond the model itself. It is only necessary to work at molar substrate concentrations far greater than the enzyme concentration and to restrict the considerations to initial rates. What remains is to develop the equations for expressing the initial reaction velocity (v_0) as a function of A for this model. In general, according to the law of mass action,

$$v = \frac{dX}{dt} = -\frac{dA}{dt} = k_{+2}(EA) - k_{-2}\,XE \tag{7}$$

where k_{+2} and k_{-2} are the rate constants for the forward and reverse directions of reaction 2 and the capital letters indicate concentrations of the designated reactants. Moreover, since only initial velocity (v_0) is to be considered, $X = 0$ and the last term of Eq. (7) becomes zero. Thus

$$v_0 = k_{+2}(EA) \tag{8}$$

Clearly, this equation must describe the initial overall velocity under all circumstances for the model under consideration. It should be noted that the expression implies a limiting maximum velocity for the reaction at sufficiently high substrate concentration, where (EA) must approach E_0. Under these conditions,

$$v_0 = k_{+2} E_0 = V \tag{9}$$

where V is the limiting or maximum velocity.

The foregoing expressions, however, are not sufficient. The direct determination of (EA) is very rarely possible. Accordingly, it is necessary to establish how (EA) varies as a function of A. A differential equation expressing the time course of (EA) may be written in a manner analogous to Eq. (7):

$$\frac{d(EA)}{dt} = k_{+1}AE - k_{-1}(EA) - k_{+2}(EA) \tag{10}$$

E can be eliminated from Eq. (10) by use of the "enzyme conservation equation,"

$$E_0 = E + (EA)$$

E is the actual concentration of *free* enzyme. To get the equations into terms of quantities knowable experimentally, we substitute for E the expression $E_0 - (EA)$, as E_0 at least will be a known quantity. The same precaution is not necessary with A since $A = A_0$ to a very good first approximation under initial conditions where $A_0 \gg E_0$ and only a miniscule fraction of A is required to form (EA). The equation thus becomes

$$\frac{d(EA)}{dt} = k_{+1}A_0[E_0 - (EA)] - k_{-1}(EA) - k_{+2}(EA) \tag{11}$$

If Eq. (11) could be solved to yield an expression for (EA) in terms of A_0, E_0, and the rate constants only, the derivation would be easily completed. Unfortunately, this cannot be done rigorously, so it is necessary to make some simplifying assumptions to achieve the desired goal. Three alternative assumptions have been made in various efforts to solve this problem:

1. Henri (5) and subsequently Michaelis and Menten (6) assumed that k_{+2} is very small relative to k_{-1}; i.e., that equilibrium is achieved in reaction 1 of Eq. (6).

2. Van Slyke and Cullen (7) assumed that k_{+2} is very large relative to k_{-1}; i.e., that reaction 1 is irreversible.

3. Briggs and Haldane (8) assumed that the rates of change in concentration of (EA) are negligible relative to the rates of change of the concentrations of A or X, which are the quantities to be measured in the system; i.e., that (EA) is in a "steady state;"

$$\frac{d(EA)}{dt} \simeq 0$$

The Henri–Michaelis–Menten and Van Slyke–Cullen developments will not be given here. There is now a considerable body of experimental evidence indicating that neither of these assumptions holds generally. The relative magnitudes of the individual rate constants in enzyme-catalyzed reactions evidently are not so restricted. As is evident from Fig. 5 and the preceding discussion, however, the steady-state approximation is a more likely basis for kinetic development.[4]

On this basis, Eq. (11) becomes

$$\frac{d(EA)}{dt} = k_{+1}A_0[E_0 - (EA)] - k_{-1}(EA) - k_{+2}(EA) = 0$$

This can be solved. We rearrange to

$$(EA)(k_{-1} + k_{+2} + k_{+1}A_0) = k_{+1}E_0 A_0 \tag{12}$$

or

$$(EA) = \left(\frac{k_{+1}}{k_{-1} + k_{+2} + k_{+1}A_0}\right)E_0 A_0 \tag{13}$$

If K_m is defined as

$$K_m = \frac{k_{-1} + k_{+2}}{k_{+1}}$$

Eq. (13) becomes

$$(EA) = \frac{E_0 A_0}{K_m + A_0} \tag{14}$$

Equation (14) is the desired expression for (EA) in terms of A_0, E_0, and constants. It may now be combined with Eq. (8) to yield the expression

$$v_0 = \frac{k_{+2} A_0 E_0}{K_m + A_0} \tag{15}$$

and then with Eq. (9) to give

$$v_0 = \frac{VA_0}{K_m + A_0} \tag{16}$$

It will be noted that when $A_0 = K_m$, $v_0 = V/2$. This provides an operational definition of K_m as the substrate concentration yielding half maximal velocity. Note, also, that K_m is independent of the enzyme concentration.

How may Eq. (16), derived using the steady-state approximation, be tested for its applicability to actual enzyme reactions? It has in fact been tested a great many times both before and after its derivation.

[4] Walter and Morales (9), Walter (10), and Wong (11) have recently examined this hypothesis critically by sophisticated techniques, finding it essentially sound for the usual experimental conditions. We shall return to this point in the last section of the chapter.

Equation (16) is identical to the Henri equation (5), given in the previous section of this chapter.

It will be noted that Eq. (16), being the equation of a rectangular hyperbola, is susceptible to algebraic manipulation to yield forms that may be plotted as straight lines. These are convenient as means of evaluating maximum velocities and Michaelis constants (K_m values) and for examining data for irregularities that may indicate difficulties in the experimental system or special features in the mechanism. The three common linear plots are illustrated in Fig. 6, with the respective slope-intercept forms of Eq. (16) and the significance of the slope and intercept values. There is a continuing discussion regarding which of these forms is the most useful in practice (12–21), as each has its own practical strengths and weaknesses, depending in part on the detailed design of the experiment. Probably most enzymologists plot their data in all three ways to take advantage of the full range of discriminatory powers available.

The plotting and the evaluation of kinetic coefficients, with their confidence limits, are best done by statistical methods, but simple least-squares analysis of the data in one of the linear plotting forms is not adequate, since inversion distorts the error span (22,23). Data *can* be handled in this form if appropriately weighted, but the best techniques seem to involve iterative fitting to the best rectangular hyperbola. Cleland has discussed the appropriate conditions and worked out computer programs for all the common cases (24).

It can scarcely be overemphasized that the coincidence of Eq. (5) and (16) does *not* demonstrate that enzymes operate by the mechanism from which the latter equation was derived. In this regard it is instructive to note that an equation of exactly the same form may be derived from the mechanism having either the special restrictions assumed by Henri and Michaelis and Menten or those assumed by Van Slyke and Cullen. Only the meanings of the constants differ and it is clear that the meanings derived from the steady-state treatment [e.g., $K_m = (k_{+2} + k_{-1})/k_{+1}$] are the most generally useful. What this development *does* demonstrate is that a mechanism of the form adopted *may* be a correct description of enzymic catalysis. Other means have been required to demonstrate the superiority of this type of mechanism over alternative possibilities. There has in fact been a considerable amount of discussion of fundamentally different mechanisms, including chain reaction mechanisms and "action at a distance," but these suggestions are now not generally thought to be applicable to enzymic catalysis. Major factors in establishing the present ideas in this area have been direct demonstrations of the occurrence of enzyme-substrate intermediates, the indispensable utility of enzyme-substrate complexes in understanding the action of

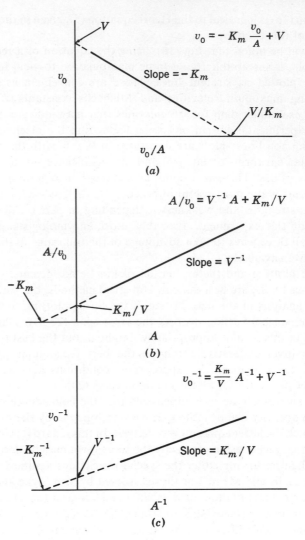

$$v_0 = -K_m \frac{v_0}{A} + V$$

Slope $= -K_m$

(a)

$$A/v_0 = V^{-1} A + K_m/V$$

Slope $= V^{-1}$

(b)

$$v_0^{-1} = \frac{K_m}{V} A^{-1} + V^{-1}$$

Slope $= K_m/V$

(c)

FIG. 6.   The linear plotting forms.

inhibitors, and documentations of the remarkably precise substrate specificities of enzymes.

VALIDITY OF THE STEADY-STATE HYPOTHESIS

A number of efforts have been made to obtain solutions for the rate equation more nearly complete than that afforded by the steady-state approximation. As will be discussed in Chap. 11, the entire time course of an enzyme-catalyzed reaction may ordinarily be well approximated by a function in which the steady-state relationship governs the bulk of the reaction time while a different function, which describes the formation of enzyme-substrate complex, governs the pre-steady-state time (25). The monograph by Hearon *et al.* in *The Enzymes* has considered this matter further (26). Hommes (27), Walter and Morales (9), and Walter (10) have combined such efforts with computer techniques to address the question whether the steady-state assumption is an adequate approximation for most practical work. The results of these investigations do certainly show that the steady-state assumption is imperfect theoretically and that an incautious worker could be misled. Indeed, the error values quoted in the Walter papers are rather alarming in the magnitudes approached for very small ratios of forward to reverse bimolecular rate constants, especially in some two-substrate mechanisms (10). On careful scrutiny, however, this work is more reassuring. When it is realized that the substrate to enzyme concentration ratio was purposely held very low (compared with most actual experiments) to emphasize the theoretical points made and that increase in this ratio greatly alleviates the imperfections in the steady-state approximation, the practical meaning of the work is seen as an exoneration of the steady-state assumption in its usual applications. Nevertheless, the warning to kineticists is clear: the ratio A_0/E_0 *must* be large (preferably 10^4 or more) unless it is known that the reverse bimolecular rate constants in the mechanism are not larger than those in the forward direction.

Wong has also recently considered questions regarding the mathematical description of the entire time course of enzyme-catalyzed reactions, with attention to the steady-state assumption (11). He notes that the essential requirement is for rapid formation of the initial complex, a condition that can certainly be met by use of a high enough substrate to enzyme concentration ratio. His practical conclusion, which he extends to cover two-substrate mechanisms as well, is that conditions permitting a linear relationship between v_0 and E_0 are suitable for application of the steady-state assumption.

GENERAL REFERENCES

Frost, A. A., and R. C. Pearson: *Kinetics and Mechanism*, Wiley, New York, 1961.

Laidler, K. J.: *The Chemical Kinetics of Enzyme Action*, Oxford, London, 1958.

Dixon, M., and E. C. Webb: *Enzymes*, 2nd ed., Academic, New York, 1964.
Reiner, J. M.: *Behavior of Enzyme Systems*, Burgess, Minneapolis, 1959.
Boyer, P. D., H. Lardy, K. Myrbäck (eds.): *The Enzymes*, 2nd ed., Vol. 1, Academic, New York, 1959.
Walter, C.: *Steady-State Applications in Enzyme Kinetics*, The Ronald Press, New York, 1965.

SPECIFIC REFERENCES

1. Wong, J. T., and C. S. Hanes: *Canad. J. Biochem. Physiol.*, **40**: 763 (1962).
2. Cleland, W. W.: *Biochim. et Biophys. Acta*, **67**: 104 (1963).
3. Wilhelmy, L.: *Ann. Physik. Chemie (Poggendorf)*, **81**: 413 and 499 (1850).
4. Brown, A. J.: *J. Chem. Soc.*, **81**: 373 (1902).
5. Henri, V.: *Lois Générales de l'action des diastases*, Hermann, Paris, 1903.
6. Michaelis, L., and M. L. Menten: *Biochem. Z.*, **49**: 333 (1913).
7. Van Slyke, D. D., and G. E. Cullen: *J. Biol. Chem.*, **19**: 141 (1914).
8. Briggs, G. E., and J. B. S. Haldane: *Biochem. J.*, **19**: 338 (1925).
9. Walter, C., and M. Morales: *J. Biol. Chem.*, **239**: 1277 (1964).
10. Walter, C.: *J. Theoret. Biol.*, **11**: 181 (1966).
11. Wong, J. T.: *J. Am. Chem. Soc.*, **87**: 1788 (1965).
12. Eadie, G. S.: *J. Biol. Chem.*, **146**: 85 (1942).
13. Hofstee, B. H. J.: *Science*, **116**: 329 (1952).
14. Laidler, K. J.: *The Chemical Kinetics of Enzyme Action*, Oxford, London, 1958, p. 65.
15. Hofstee, B. H. J.: *Nature*, **184**: 1296 (1959).
16. Dixon, M., and E. C. Webb: *Nature*, **184**: 1298 (1959).
17. Hofstee, B. H. J.: *Science*, **131**: 39 (1960).
18. Wiegand, J. H.: *Science*, **131**: 1068 (1960).
19. Dixon, M., and E. C. Webb: *Enzymes*, 2nd ed., Academic, New York, 1964, p. 70.
20. Coleman, M. H.: *Nature*, **205**: 798 (1965).
21. Dowd, J. E., and D. S. Riggs: *J. Biol. Chem.*, **240**: 863 (1965).
22. Wilkinson, G. N.: *Biochem. J.*, **80**: 324 (1961).
23. Johansen, G., and R. Lumry: *Compt. Rend. Trav. Lab. Carlsberg*, **32**: 185 (1961).
24. Cleland, W. W.: *Advan. Enzymol.*, **29**: 1 (1967).
25. Roughton, F. J.: *Discussions Faraday Soc.*, **17**: 116 (1954).
26. Hearon, J., S. Bernhard, S. Friess, D. Botts, and M. Morales: in P. D. Boyer, H. Lardy, and K. Myrbäck (eds.): *The Enzymes*, 2nd ed., Vol. 1, Academic, New York, 1959.
27. Hommes, F. A.: *Arch. Biochem. Biophys.*, **96**: 28 (1962).

3

ENZYME-SUBSTRATE
INTERMEDIATES

The existence of enzyme-substrate complexes is accepted almost as axiomatic by modern enzymologists. There is presently a great wealth of kinetic and other data pertaining to enzyme-catalyzed reactions, all of it consistent with such complex formation and much of it very difficult to explain on other bases. Some of the most impressive observations to this point have been a number of direct demonstrations of enzyme-substrate combinations. These range in time from the early (1880) observation of the precipitation of papain by its substrate fibrin (1) to the recent examination by electron spin resonance and optical techniques of a crystalline enzyme-substrate intermediate of D-amino acid oxidase (2–5). The classic examples are the hemoproteins peroxidase and catalase (6,7), where direct spectroscopic evidence for the occurrence of enzymic intermediates was obtained more than 30 years ago (8,9). More recently various techniques have been used to secure direct evidence for such intermediates in the reactions catalyzed by a number of hydrolytic enzymes (10–14), aldolases (15,16), several dehydrogenases (17–21), and the sulfur transferase rhodanese (22,23).

In many of the best-established cases, however, it has been made clear that the enzymic intermediate characterized is not the simple addition complex assumed in deriving enzyme kinetic equations but rather a covalent compound formed between enzyme and a moiety that originates in the substrate but is no longer the intact substrate. Insufficient attention has often been accorded this possibility when evidence of enzymic intermediates has been reported. In at least some of the cases, however, there is clear evidence indicating occurrence of simple addition complexes between enzyme and intact substrate, and the concept of the enzyme-substrate complex has become firmly established as a useful description at one level of intellectual resolution.

The general picture involved is one in which enzyme and substrate molecules diffuse together and the rate of collision is thus diffusion-controlled. Molecular orientations on collision and various other factors discussed below determine what proportion of the collisions results in binding. It is entirely possible that a number of isomers of the enzyme-substrate complex may be formed.

There is also considerable evidence indicating that finer resolution of the problem will show the actual kinetic complexes to be complex indeed, each subsuming a number of (or a continuum of) electronic states and possibly even several forms that are chemically distinguishable. These refinements should not, however, invalidate the concept of the enzyme-substrate complex as an entity or the kinetics developed through its use.

The discussion that follows reviews the kinds of bonding that might be expected to be involved in enzyme-substrate complex formation. It then presents a few specific examples of direct evidence for the occurrence of simple enzyme-substrate addition complexes.

THE BINDING OF OTHER MOLECULES TO PROTEINS

The formation of enzyme-substrate complexes must generally entail the bonding of the molecules involved by weak forces. Furthermore, since the products of the enzymic reaction are in general similar to the substrates and yet must be discharged from the enzyme surface, complex formation would be expected to be readily reversible. With these expectations and an awareness of the properties of proteins at hand, we should find it possible to predict from the chemical nature of a particular substrate the probable bases for its complexing interaction with an enzyme. Thus the formation of complexes where the substrate is also a protein must involve the same multiplicity of forces that are active in stabilizing tertiary and quaternary structure in proteins generally. Accordingly, it is only with the much simpler, small-molecular substrates that an effort to distinguish the individual forces in "pure" form seems likely to be successful. Here, the binding by proteins of many small molecules, e.g., inorganic ions and some aromatic structures, has been studied quite apart from considerations of enzyme action. A number of features with evident significance for enzyme-substrate complex formation have been observed.

Small ions interact with proteins without obvious regard for the total net charge on the protein molecule. For example, a protein in solution at a pH where it demonstrably bears a net negative charge (i.e., on the alkaline side of its isoelectric point) can still bind small anions. Proteins can, and commonly do, bind both cations and anions at pH values over the whole range significant for enzyme action. Furthermore, this binding can be mainly ionic in character. These facts are consequences of the relative sizes of the proteins and the ions in question; a small ion can "see" at one time only a small portion of the much larger protein structure. The ionic interactions involved, then (as well as the other interactions of small molecules with proteins), are highly localized, involving only small portions of the protein surface. This example is by no means trivial since a great many substrates are small ions and ionic interactions have at once the strength and the ready reversibility to be useful in enzyme-substrate complex formation.

There is a considerable degree of specificity and even of stereo-specificity in the binding of small molecules by proteins generally. With ions, some of this specificity is based on the simple ion exchanger properties of the protein molecule, showing greater binding affinity for more highly charged ions or, with ions of the same charge, for those with smaller hydrated ionic diameters. Even with ions, however, there is specificity that must be accounted for on other bases, evidently relating to the juxtaposition of side-chain functional groups in the protein structure. An example is the formation of chelating sites, which display selectivity on the basis of the different geometries of coordinate bonding. This picture of a chelation site is easily generalized to provide the concept of sites at a similar level of complexity capable of relatively great specificity on the basis of polydentate binding. For example, a region of the protein surface containing a cationic lysyl ε-ammonium group near a region of largely nonpolar side-chain residues might be selective for fatty acid anions. Sites can also be envisioned that would be selective for one member of an enantiomorphic pair. These could involve either three attachment points for the substrate or two attachments and a steric blockage. This matter is treated further in Chap. 5.

The foregoing discussion places considerable emphasis on ion–ion interactions because of their relatively clear-cut basis and because almost all proposed mechanisms for actual enzyme-catalyzed reactions have included such interactions, but this should not be taken to indicate that many other forces are not involved. In fact, all of the forces involved in protein tertiary and quaternary structure, singly or in combinations, may be brought into play in complex formation between proteins and small molecules. The possibilities for hydrophobic bonding and direct interactions involving London dispersion forces, that together may amount practically to a dissolution of all or a part of a nonpolar sub-strate molecule in a nonpolar area of the enzyme surface, have already been mentioned. It is also probable that hydrogen bonding is important, especially when it can be polyfunctional or combined with other binding forces.

Some additional possibilities outside the forces usually considered prominent in protein–protein interactions are probably important in the formation of some complexes. Ion-dipole interactions are very likely of importance, and these must include induced dipoles as well, since many substrates bear easily polarizable groupings. Charge transfer interactions also probably occur in many cases as there are substrates, including some coenzymes, that are notably good charge transfer acceptors.

In all of these interactions account must be taken of limiting steric factors, based on the allowable bond angles and the mutual repulsions of the "van der Waals shells" of the atoms; i.e., repulsions caused by the close approach of the electron clouds of atoms. Finally, consideration must be given the role of the solvent in the energy changes accompanying binding. In aqueous solutions ions and dipoles exert a polarizing effect on water molecules. Some of these water molecules are relatively firmly bound to each ion or dipole, resulting in a decrease of volume relative to pure water, an effect called electrostriction. When two ions of opposite sign come together, with the resulting formation of a neutral molecule, considerable water is released from its oriented condition. This appears thermodynamically as an increase in entropy. In the opposite case, when ions of like sign combine to make an ion of higher charge, the electrostrictive effect of the latter is so large that a net decrease in entropy results. Qualitatively similar (but quantitatively much smaller) changes occur in cases involving dipoles. It has been calculated that the molar entropy change arising from the electrostriction effect in dilute aqueous solution is roughly 10 entropy units for interactions between two singly charged ions. This amounts to a contribution to the free energy of reaction of about 3 kcal at ordinary temperatures. Since the energy changes involved increase as the product of the charges, it should be clear that in the interaction between a multiply cationic active site and a dianion, for example, the electrostriction effect may be far from negligible.

It seems probable that fully covalent bonding of an intact substrate in enzyme-substrate complex formation does not occur. A number of cases are known, however, in which the enzyme does form a covalent intermediate with a transferable group originating in a substrate. In some cases the group transferred is only a single atom; in others it is all of the substrate molecule except a single atom. The important point is that this covalent type of intermediate, which arises by rupture of a bond in the substrate and formation of a new bond between the enzyme and a part of the substrate, is qualitatively different from the simple enzyme-substrate addition complex. The striking kinetic consequences of this distinction are treated in Chap. 8.

The forces involved in true enzyme-substrate complex formation, then, may encompass practically all the kinds of molecular interaction in which proteins may engage, probably excluding only covalent bonding. It is to be noted also that an enzyme, by binding certain cofactors, may dramatically increase its capabilities for substrate binding; e.g., by coordination or chelation of a metal ion to create a powerfully cationic site.

DIRECT EVIDENCE FOR ENZYME-SUBSTRATE ADDITION COMPLEXES

While it has been possible in many cases to obtain convincing kinetic evidence for the existence of true enzyme-substrate complexes, suitable direct confirmatory evidence has been secured in relatively few instances. Such observations are of major importance, however, for they establish unequivocally that addition complexes do occur as intermediates in enzyme-catalyzed reactions. All modern theoretical developments in enzymology presume their existence.

Some of the most impressive direct observations to this point have been reported for combinations of enzymes with their coenzymes.[1] In lactic dehydrogenase, for example, Velick showed that formation of complexes between the enzyme and either the oxidized or the reduced form of the NAD coenzyme causes marked changes in the fluorescence emission and fluorescence polarization properties of the components (24). The fluorescence polarization evidence is especially impressive since these data depend on the molecular size of the fluorescing structure. The polarization change is striking when a molecule of pyridine nucleotide becomes associated with a molecule of protein. That these changes refer to the formation of simple addition complexes rather than intermediate compounds of the substituted enzyme variety is clear from the analysis of kinetic data (25) showing that the mechanism does not involve such a compound. A ternary complex involving enzyme, coenzyme, and lactate is attained before discharge of any product. (See Chaps. 7–9 for the basis for such kinetic inference.) Other physical

---

[1] It should be clear that a coenzyme is in fact a substrate of the enzymes with which it functions, formally differing from other substrates only in being a substrate of more than one enzyme, in such a way that it is cyclically regenerated.

evidence for the existence of lactic dehydrogenase-coenzyme complexes has been obtained using spectroscopic methods (26) and ultracentrifugal separation techniques (27). Moreover, the demonstration of direct transfer of hydrogen from the lactate to the coenzyme (28) requires formulation of the reaction as involving obligatory formation of a ternary complex of the enzyme with both substrates.

For yeast alcohol dehydrogenase, also, there is impressive kinetic (29), fluorescence (24), centrifugal (30), and direct transfer (31) evidence indicating that enzyme–coenzyme addition complex formation is a physical reality. Similarly for liver alcohol dehydrogenase, there is spectral (32), kinetic (33), and direct transfer (34) evidence to this point. Glyceraldehyde-3-phosphate dehydrogenase has also been studied in great detail. It is ordinarily isolated with its NAD attached but readily removable. The fluorescence and absorbance properties (30, 35), the centrifugal evidence (36), the kinetic data (37), and the direct hydrogen transfer evidence (34) all clearly indicate the existence of enzyme-substrate addition complexes. For such cases no alternative formulation fits all of the evidence reasonably well.

Lest it be thought from the foregoing that coenzymes are a special class of substrates, distinguished by more than their special convenience for this purpose, it must be pointed out that there are other cases as well as other convincing kinds of evidence. For example, comparison of the X-ray crystallographic structure of carboxypeptidase A and its complex with glycyl-L-tyrosine at the 2–3 Å level of resolution (38) shows not only the actual position of the bound peptide in a "hydrophobic pocket" in the enzyme but also such intimate details as the fact that an enzymic tyrosyl residue moves about 14 Å toward the substrate on complex formation. A similar extremely impressive case in point is that involving the X-ray crystallographic (39) and mechanistic (40) correlations for lysozyme. Here, as with carboxypeptidase, the structures of both free enzyme and complex are known in great detail.

As a further example, one of the crystalline intermediates isolated by Yagi *et al.* (2–5) from anaerobic reaction mixtures of D-amino acid oxidase appears to be a true enzyme-substrate addition complex. The evidence strongly suggests that the diamagnetic purple crystalline intermediate isolated is such a complex. Treatment with benzoate under anaerobic conditions fully dissociates this complex to substrate and the benzoate complex of the oxidized enzyme. The optical rotatory dispersion and circular dichroism data indicate substrate binding to the isoalloxazine nucleus of the prosthetic group, and the accompanying spectral changes suggest charge transfer association as the mode of binding. Subsequently, as the transfer of an electron is completed, a second crystalline complex containing paramagnetic semiquinoid forms can be isolated, but there seems to be no reason to doubt the status of the first form as a classical enzyme-substrate addition complex.

Finally, the elegant spectrophotometric work of Chance on the hemoprotein enzymes must be cited. Although this work has been of great importance in the development of our ideas on enzymic catalysis, it is so well known and widely discussed that it does not require extensive review here. The fundamental observation was of the occurrence of changes in the absorption spectra of the iron porphyrin prosthetic group. With peroxidase the existence of no fewer than four different enzymic complexes involving the substrate hydrogen peroxide was demonstrated. There has not been universal agreement, however, as to the chemical nature of all of these complexes. For example, whereas Chance (41) has formulated the first complex as a simple addition complex, George (42) has disputed this view, suggesting that the ferric iron in the porphyrin is further oxidized at the first step:

$$Fe^{3+} \text{protoporphyrin} + H_2O_2 \rightarrow Fe^{3+}O \text{ protoporphyrin} + H_2O$$

Although the status of the peroxidase-H_2O_2 intermediates as simple addition complexes has thus been questioned, there is nonetheless great value in the level of resolution to which this work has been carried, sufficient to suggest that several, perhaps many, distinct complex states may be the rule.

There are in the rapidly growing literature of this field many more examples of direct observations of physical changes accompanying the addition of substrates to enzymes involving spectral techniques (43), electron spin resonance methods and techniques suitable for detecting protein conformational changes. In reading this literature, however, it is important to bear in mind that there is a genuine distinction between enzyme-substrate addition complexes and substituted enzyme inter-mediates. This is a distinction that can ordinarily be made experimentally on a kinetic basis (Chap. 8), but unless the necessary kinetic work is also cited, a reported instance of a " Michaelis complex," as they are sometimes called, must be considered only provisional until the formal nature of the mechanism has been clarified. It needs to be stressed, however, that even mechanisms in which a substituted enzyme inter-mediate is formed must generally also include one or two intermediate binary complexes of the simple addition variety. Two examples showing how the existence of the addition complexes is evident in such cases are glutamic-oxalacetic transaminase (44) and rhodanese (45).

The current status of the true enzyme-substrate addition complex, then, is essentially that of a fact. The physical existence of such entities is so firmly established, on the joint bases of direct observation, kinetic inference and chemical plausibility, that the enzymologist's acceptance of them is unshakeable.

GENERAL REFERENCES

Chance, B.: *Advan. Enzymol.*, **12**: 153 (1951).

Boyer, P. D., H. Lardy, and K. Myrbäck (eds.): *The Enzymes*, 2nd ed., Vol. 7, Academic, New York, 1963.

SPECIFIC REFERENCES

1. Wurtz, A.: *Compt. rend.*, **91**: 787 (1880).
2. Yagi, K., and T. Ozawa: *Biochim. Biophys. Acta*, **81**: 29 (1964).
3. Yagi, K., and T. Ozawa: *Nature*, **203**: 864 (1964).
4. Yagi, K., and K. Okamura: *J. Biochem. (Japan)*, **58**: 417 (1965).
5. Yagi, K., and N. Sugiura: *J. Biochem. (Japan)*, **60**: 738 (1966).
6. Chance, B.: *J. Biol. Chem.*, **151**: 553 (1943).
7. Chance, B.: *Acta Chem. Scand.*, **1**: 236 (1947).
8. Stern, K. G.: *J. Biol. Chem.*, **114**: 473 (1936).
9. Keilin, D., and T. Mann: *Proc. Roy. Soc. (London), Ser. B.*, **122**: 119 (1936).
10. Balls, A. K., and H. N. Wood: *J. Biol. Chem.*, **219**: 245 (1956).
11. Bender, M. L., G. R. Schonbaum, and B. Zerner: *J. Am. Chem. Soc.*, **84**: 2540 (1962).
12. Bernhard, S. A., S. J. Lau, and H. Noller: *Biochemistry*, **4**: 1108 and 1118 (1965).
13. Engstrom, L.: *Biochim. Biophys. Acta*, **52**: 49 (1961) and **54**: 179 (1961).
14. Schwartz, J. H., and F. Lipmann: *Proc. Natl. Acad. Sci. U.S.*, **47**: 1996 (1961).
15. Horecker, B. L., S. Pontrenoli, C. Ricci, and T. Cheng: *Proc. Natl. Acad. Sci. U.S.*, **47**: 1949 (1961).
16. Horecker, B. L., P. T. Rowley, E. Grazi, T. Cheng, and O. Tchola: *Biochem. Z.*, **338**: 36 (1963).
17. Theorell, H., and R. Bonnichsen: *Acta. Chem. Scand.*, **5**: 1105 (1951).
18. Theorell, H., and B. Chance: *Acta. Chem. Scand.*, **5**: 1127 (1951).
19. Chance, B., and J. B. Neilands: *J. Biol. Chem.*, **199**: 383 (1952).
20. Racker, E., and I. Krimsky: *J. Biol. Chem.*, **198**: 731 (1952).
21. Velick, S. F.: *J. Biol. Chem.*, **203**: 563 (1953).
22. Green, J. R., and J. Westley: *J. Biol. Chem.*, **236**: 3047 (1961).
23. Westley, J., and T. Nakamoto: *J. Biol. Chem.*, **237**: 547 (1962).
24. Velick, S. F.: *J. Biol. Chem.*, **233**: 1455 (1958).
25. Schwert, G. W., B. R. Miller, and P. J. Peanasky: *J. Biol. Chem.*, **242**: 3245 (1967).

26. Chance, B., and J. B. Neilands: *J. Biol. Chem.*, **199**: 383 (1952).
27. Takenaka, Y., and G. W. Schwert: *J. Biol. Chem.*, **223**: 157 (1956).
28. Loewus, F. A., P. Ofner, H. F. Fisher, F. H. Westheimer, and B. Vennesland: *J. Biol. Chem.*, **202**: 699 (1953).
29. Wrattan, C. C., and W. W. Cleland: *Biochemistry*, **2**: 935 (1963).
30. Velick, S. F., J. E. Hayes, and J. Harting: *J. Biol. Chem.*, **203**: 527 (1953).
31. Fisher, H. F., E. E. Conn, B. Vennesland, and F. H. Westheimer: *J. Biol. Chem.*, **202**: 687 (1953).
32. Theorell, H., and R. Bonnichsen: *Acta Chem. Scand.*, **5**: 329 (1951).
33. Theorell, H., and A. S. McKinley McKee: *Acta Chem. Scand.*, **15**: 1797ff (1961).
34. Levy, H. R., and B. Vennesland: *J. Biol. Chem.*, **228**: 85 (1957).
35. Smith, T. E.: *Biochemistry*, **5**: 2919 (1966).
36. Velick, S. F.: *J. Biol. Chem.*, **203**: 563 (1953).
37. Velick, S. F., and C. Furfine: in P. D. Boyer, H. Lardy, and K. Myrbäck (eds.), *The Enzymes*, 2nd ed., Vol. 7, 1963.
38. Reeke, G. N., J. A. Hartsuck, M. L. Ludwig, F. A. Quiocho, T. A. Steitz, and W. N. Lipscomb: *Proc. Natl. Acad. Sci. U.S.*, **58**: 2220 (1967).
39. Blake, C. C. F., G. A. Mair, A. C. T. North, D. C. Phillips, and V. R. Sarma: *Proc. Roy. Soc. (London), Ser. B*, **167**: 378 (1967).
40. Blake, C. C. F., L. N. Johnson, G. A. Mair, A. C. T. North, D. C. Phillips, and V. R. Sarma: *Proc. Roy. Soc. (London), Ser. B*, **167**: 385 (1967).
41. Chance, B.: *Arch. Biochem. Biophys.*, **41**: 416 (1952).
42. George, P.: *Biochem. J.*, **55**: 220 (1953).
43. Ishimura, Y., M. Nozaki, and O. Hayaishi: *J. Biol. Chem.*, **242**, 2574 (1967).
44. Henson, C. P., and W. W. Cleland: *Biochemistry*, **3**: 338 (1964).
45. Volini, M., and J. Westley: *J. Biol. Chem.*, **241**: 5168 (1966).

4

INHIBITION, ACTIVATION, INACTIVATION, pH EFFECTS

A very substantial portion of the work done in enzymology has been concerned with the effects of "foreign" substances on enzymic reaction systems. This is hardly surprising in view of the practical aspects of the question from the economic and pharmacological points of view. What is perhaps not so well known, however, is the important role that inhibition may play in the analysis of fundamental mechanisms. This is especially true when the inhibiting or activating substance is not really "foreign" but is instead a proton, a substrate or product of the reaction under study, or a metabolite involved in other reactions in the same cell. As an introductory basis for considering such effects, the discussion that follows is a systematic development of the logical consequences of introducing into our simple one-substrate reaction scheme a foreign substance that can interact with one or more of the components. This development will also provide a basis on which to build in later chapters an intuitive understanding of the kinetics of two-substrate reaction systems.

As there are only three components that are significant for initial velocities in the one-substrate reaction system, there are only three possible primary points of attack for an inhibiting or activating substance. These are indicated in Fig. 7. For purposes of discussion, we shall consider the three parts separately and then in combination.

SUBSTANCES THAT COMBINE WITH THE FREE ENZYME

The circle numbered 1 in Fig. 7 encloses a schematic representation of one kind of interaction of a substance Q with an enzymic reaction system. Here Q acts by combining reversibly with the enzyme to create

42

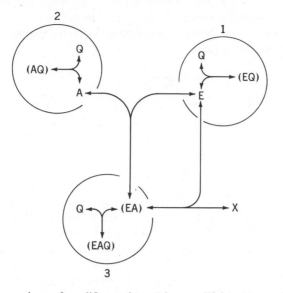

FIG. 7. The regions of modifier action. Q is a modifying compound that can combine with a component of the catalytic reaction cycle. Action in each of these areas is considered separately (see text).

a form which is inactive in combining with the substrate A. Q, then, is an inhibitor. It will be noted that we have thus made three special assumptions about Q: (a) that the combination is reversible, (b) that it combines exclusively with the free enzyme, and (c) that (EQ) is totally inactive. Later on we shall be at pains to distinguish what the effects will be if any of these conditions is not met. For the present, let us insert Q into our kinetic equations for the case as stated.

This is easily done. The entire effect of Q is in introducing an additional term into Eq. (11) of Chap. 2, which includes a statement of all of the forms of the enzyme. For this case: $E_0 = E + (EA) + (EQ)$. Since (EQ) is a "dead end," the concentration of this form can be stated in terms of a simple equilibrium constant:[1] $K_Q = (EQ)/QE$, and $(EQ) = K_Q QE$. On this basis, the steady-state derivation of the initial velocity expression requires the replacement of the term E of Eq. (10) by the term $[E_0 - (EA)]/(QK_Q + 1)$, rather than simply by $E_0 - (EA)$ as before. The difference in reaction schemes, then, is reflected solely by the occurrence of the denominator term $(QK_Q + 1)$. As the derivation

[1] The reader is fairly warned that different authors formulate these "inhibitor constants" differently. For example, Dixon and Webb's K_i is the inverse of Laidler's K_i, the former being a dissociation constant, the latter an association constant like the K_Q of the present development.

is carried through exactly as before, with steps entirely analogous to
Eq. (12–16) of Chap. 2, the new denominator term persists, appearing
in the final rate equation

$$v_0 = \frac{VA_0}{K_m(QK_Q + 1) + A_0} \tag{17}$$

This result makes clear the nature of the inhibition: the equation is
of the same form (i.e., the linear plots are still linear); the maximum
velocity is unaltered; and the apparent Michaelis constant is increased
relative to the uninhibited situation, by the factor $(QK_Q + 1)$. It is
evident that K_Q can be evaluated experimentally on this basis, since
determinations in the absence of Q yield K_m and those in its presence
yield $K_m(QK_Q + 1)$.[2] When Q is zero or when K_Q is very small, indicating
a low affinity of Q for the enzyme, no inhibition is evident and the apparent K_m is normal. Moreover, then A_0 is so large that it dominates the
denominator of Eq. (17), i.e., as the substrate concentration approaches
that yielding the maximum velocity condition, the QK_Q term is again
without effect, so that the normal V is never obscured. Because of the
form of the denominator of Eq. (17), then, the inhibitory effect has a
"competitive" appearance, being at its greatest at high inhibitor or
low substrate concentration and disappearing as either the inhibitor
concentration becomes very small or the substrate concentration becomes
very high. These conclusions are reflected in the differences between the
normal and competitively inhibited plots shown in Fig. 8.

This "competitive" appearance *can* be the result of a competitive
process. The simplest mechanism for this type of behavior is a literal
competition between A and Q for the same binding sites on the enzyme.
Actually, of course, any form of combination that makes the binding of
A and Q mutually exclusive processes will yield the same kinetic result.
Moreover, as we shall see below, other phenomena may also give this
result, and caution is required in the interpretation of inhibitor data.

Before going on, however, consider what would result if the reaction
of Q with E were practically irreversible (i.e., if the dissociation of (EQ)
were slow compared with the assay procedure). Clearly, this would
result simply in a diminution of total enzyme concentration, to an
extent depending on the total available quantity of Q. No amount of A
would have any restoring effect in this situation; E_0 would just be
lowered. It follows that V, which equals $k_{+2}E_0$, would be lowered in
proportion to the decrease in E_0 but K_m would not be affected, as no
enzyme concentration term appears in K_m.

[2] A graphical procedure is discussed below in connection with noncompetitive
inhibition.

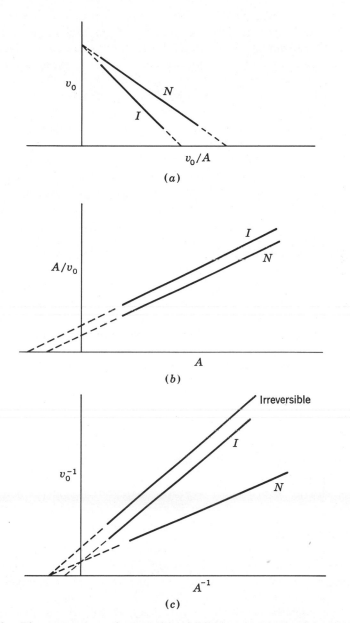

FIG. 8. The appearance of competitive inhibition. For each of the plotting forms, the normal and inhibited systems are marked N and I, respectively. The irreversible case is shown in (c) only.

This case, then, would have the appearance noted in Fig. 8 as "irreversible." It is usually distinguished from inhibition by being called "inactivation." In practice, however, the distinction has not always been attended. This is unfortunate, as the kinetic appearance is superficially like pure "noncompetitive" inhibition, which proceeds from different causes.[3] It is especially to be noted that for the irreversible case, nothing whatever can be concluded regarding the sites of inhibitor binding, which may or may not relate to the substrate binding sites. All of these considerations, with exactly the same results, also apply to the case of irreversible combination in region 3 of our diagram (Fig. 7). Thus the foregoing description of consequences applies to all instances of irreversible combination with the enzyme, whether or not it is laden with substrate.

SUBSTANCES THAT COMBINE WITH THE SUBSTRATE

Consider the region numbered 2 in Fig. 7. There the substance Q is such that it combines exclusively with the free substrate. Under these circumstances our equations require modification on the basis that A is now *not* approximately equal to A_0 but is diminished by the amount of (AQ). The latter concentration can be expressed in terms of an equilibrium constant in the same fashion as EQ of the preceding development: $(AQ) = QAK_Q$. Then

$$A = A_0 - (AQ) = A_0 - QAK_Q = \frac{A_0}{QK_Q + 1}$$

and again there is a denominator term of the same form as before. Also as before, the $(QK_Q + 1)$ denominator term carries through into the final rate equation

$$v_0 = \frac{VA_0}{K_m(QK_Q + 1) + A_0} \tag{17a}$$

which is identical to Eq. (17).

It is perhaps not surprising to find that reversible combination with the substrate yields the same result (Fig. 9) as classical competitive inhibition since in this case Q may reasonably be said to compete with

[3] This distinction can be made experimentally, however, on two different bases. Kinetically, as we shall see, both the slopes and the intercepts of double reciprocal plots for noncompetitive inhibition must vary linearly with inhibitor concentration, whereas the irreversible case yields nonlinear secondary plots of this sort. Alternatively, the experimenter may make direct tests of reversibility (e.g., testing for reactivation of the inhibited enzyme when Q is removed from solution by molecular filtration techniques).

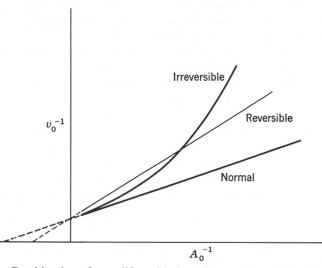

v_0^{-1}

Irreversible

Reversible

Normal

A_0^{-1}

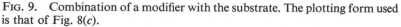

FIG. 9.   Combination of a modifier with the substrate. The plotting form used
is that of Fig. 8(c).

the enzyme for the substrate. The applicability of this result does,
however, depend on how the reaction is followed. If the substrate
concentration A_0 is taken simply as the concentration put into the
reaction mixture and the velocity v_0 is determined by following the rate
at which the product X appears, Q will not be kinetically distinguishable
from a true competitive inhibitor. Only if A_0 is in fact *measured* in the
complete reaction mixture by a method capable of distinguishing free A
from (AQ) and if v_0 is determined as the rate of disappearance of A
(and, preferably, at the same time as the rate of appearance of X) will
Q be seen as innocuous for the enzyme itself.

Again, this distinction between competitive effects has not always
been properly attended. One often finds reports which give kinetic
curves looking like the normal and reversible cases of Fig. 8 or Fig. 9,
with the tentative conclusion that the inhibitor acts at the substrate
binding site of the enzyme. In view of the above results, however, the
minimal additional requirement for such a conclusion would seem to be
a demonstration that the inhibitor does not react significantly with the
substrate, even by ion pair formation or other freely reversible processes.
Actually, it should also be shown, by use of several concentrations of Q,
that K_Q is in fact a constant, as other phenomena (e.g., ionic strength
effects) may qualitatively mimic competitive inhibition but reveal
themselves to be otherwise only in an inconstant apparent K_Q.

It remains to be considered what the result would be if Q combined with A irreversibly. In this case, A_0 is simply diminished by the amount of Q present. The equations and plots relating v_0 to $(A_0 - Q)$ are normal, but plots relating v_0 to A_0, where A_0 is simply the concentration of substrate put into the reaction mixture, cannot be of the normal type. The rectangular hyperbola that is the plot of v_0 against A_0 is displaced on the A_0 axis and all of the linear form plots are nonlinear (Fig. 9). The occurrence of this phenomenon, then, should at least not be misleading in the sense of mimicking a normal inhibitor form. On the other hand, we shall see that the appearance of this curve is by no means diagnostic, as there are many other possible causes of nonlinear plots of this type,[4] including mixtures of enzymes, multivalent enzymes with interacting sites and some perfectly normal two-substrate mechanisms.

SUBSTANCES THAT COMBINE EXCLUSIVELY WITH THE ENZYME-SUBSTRATE COMPLEX

Region 3 of Fig. 7 encloses a type of reaction that seems rather unlikely to occur in pure form. It supposes that there can be a substance Q which interacts reversibly with the enzyme-substrate complex but with neither the free enzyme nor the free substrate. This is obviously possible but it must be relatively rare. Nevertheless, it will be instructive to consider the kinetic results of such a mechanism, for essentially the same plots are obtained for at least three other mechanistic situations that undoubtedly do occur often.

As in the previous development, the only feature of the normal kinetic formulation that is directly affected in the present instance is the statement of the total number of forms of the enzyme. It is necessary in this case to include the concentration of (EAQ). This, in turn, depends on the value of the equilibrium constant K_Q for the association and on the concentrations of (EA) and Q. As before, the situation can be expressed in the equation by inserting a term representing the concentration of the new chemical form: $(EAQ) = (EA)(Q)K_Q$, and our fundamental Eq. 11 now has the form

$$\frac{d(EA)}{dt} = k_{+1}A_0[E_0 - (EA) - (EA)QK_Q] - k_{-1}(EA) - k_{+2}(EA) = 0$$

[4] In principle, the irreversible case gives a double reciprocal plot that goes to infinite slope (zero velocity) at a real concentration of A and is thus unlike the other cases cited. Whether this difference can be distinguished experimentally, however, depends on the details of the assay system used.

When the necessary transpositions are made and (EA) is taken out, it is clear that once again we have a denominator term of the form $(QK_Q + 1)$. This time, however, the final rate equation has a slightly different form

$$v_0 = \frac{VA_0}{K_m + A_0(QK_Q + 1)} = \frac{A_0 V/(QK_Q + 1)}{K_m/(QK_Q + 1) + A_0} \tag{18}$$

What has happened is simply the multiplication of both K_m and V by the same factor $(QK_Q + 1)^{-1}$. The equation still describes a rectangular hyperbola and the "linear plots" are proper straight lines. Such plots at different Q concentrations would share with the uninhibited case the abscissa intercept in the plot of type (a) in Fig. 6 and the ordinate intercept in plot (b). No points are shared in the double reciprocal plot (c), which gives parallel lines for this case (Fig. 10).

The foregoing type of kinetic behavior is referred to as "uncompetitive" inhibition. It could in principle arise from the cause for which we have derived the equations. There are at least three other circumstances, however, that could yield the same behavior. It will be shown in Chapt. 8 that the kinetics of two-substrate reactions involving substituted enzyme intermediates would yield plots of this character if Q reacted with one of the free substrates rather than with an enzyme-substrate complex. Consider also the special case of the one-substrate reaction in which $k_{+2} \gg k_{-1}$, so that $K_m \simeq k_{+2}/k_{+1}$ (corresponding to the Van Slyke–Cullen assumption). In this case any Q that affects only k_{+2} must have proportionate effects on K_m and V, which equals $k_{+2}E_0$.

Finally, the case of substrate "wrong way binding" or "misorientation" requires consideration. This phenomenon, which probably occurs frequently in studies involving synthetic analogue substrates (1–4), arises from an ambiguity with regard to the attachment of the substrate to the enzyme. Suppose that an enzyme **E** has two groups **e** and **f** which normally combine with the respective groups in substrate **e'f'**, as in Fig. 11(a). Assume, however, that there is a substrate, say **e″f'**, in which **e″** has an electronic or structural similarity to **f'**. The result will be that some of the enzyme-substrate complexes formed will be "backward," i.e., will contain misoriented substrate [Fig. 11(b)], and will fail to give rise to product. The effect of this phenomenon will be an inhibition relative to the normal case.

The form of this result is easily derived. If we assume **e'f'** and **e″f'** to have properties as substrates that are otherwise identical, this is simply a competitive inhibition mechanism in which Q is, however, the substrate itself. Accordingly, we can simply replace Q in Eq. (17)

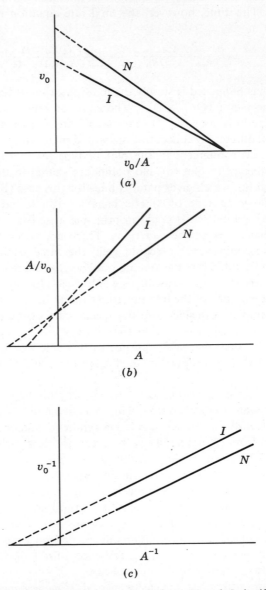

FIG. 10. Uncompetitive inhibition. As before, N and I signify "normal" and "inhibited," respectively.

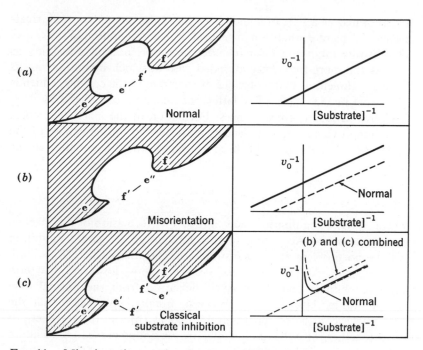

FIG. 11. Misorientation and substrate inhibition. The shaded area in each case represents the surface of the enzyme molecule. **e** and **f**, active site groups; **e'–f'** and **e"–f'**, substrate molecules.

by A_0, leaving K_Q as the equilibrium constant for the formation of the misoriented complex. This yields

$$v_0 = \frac{VA_0}{K_m(A_0 K_Q + 1) + A_0} = \frac{VA_0}{K_m + A_0(K_Q K_m + 1)} = \frac{A_0 V/(K_Q K_m + 1)}{K_m/(K_Q K_m + 1) + A_0} \quad (19)$$

This result, then, has formal similarity to uncompetitive inhibition in that substrates **e'f'** and **e"f'** would give parallel reciprocal plots. Notice should be taken of the implication that **e"f'** will give not only a lower V but also a lower K_m than does **e'f'**. Thus, for two substrates having exactly equal affinities for the enzyme as substrates, the one which also possesses the inhibitory misorienting property has the *lower* K_m to the extent that $K_Q K_m$ is significant relative to one. For this reason, among others, decisions regarding the "natural" substrates for enzymes simply on the basis that they should have the lowest K_m values are obviously invalid.

The idea that single molecules of some substrates may form inactive complexes with an enzyme is by no means new. It has been incorporated as a part of some (5–7), but unfortunately not all, treatments of substrate inhibition in general. Full consideration of the causes of substrate inhibition must include the misorientation possibility as well as the more frequently attended case in which inhibition results from attachment of two molecules of substrate to the enzyme, which is illustrated in Fig. 11(c).[5] The latter phenomenon, considered by itself has obvious kinetic consequences. Formation of the inactive complex containing two substrate molecules must depend on the square of the substrate concentration. This term appears in the rate equation in the form

$$v_0 = \frac{VA}{K_m + A + K_Q A^2}$$

where K_Q is the equilibrium constant for the formation of the inactive ternary complex. According to this mechanism, substrate inhibition will be no problem at low substrate concentrations where $K_Q A^2$ will be very small. At high substrate concentrations, however, this term will predominate and the marked deviation from the normal case shown in Fig. 11(c) will be observed. Finally, note again that the phenomena considered separately in Fig. 11 (b) and (c) are likely to occur together, with the result shown by the dotted curve in (c). Failure to bear this in mind would result in misinterpretation of the K_m and V values obtained by extrapolation of the linear portion of such curves. In general, the extrapolation of the linear portions of plots showing substrate inhibition will *not* serve as a means for obtaining values of K_m and V defined without reference to the inhibition constant.

Inhibition By Products. The progress of an enzyme-catalyzed reaction may be slowed in the presence of a product of that reaction for any of several reasons (8). One of these is the overall reversal of the reaction so that there is some loss of product and corresponding synthesis of substrate. Such a phenomenon, however, is not generally a useful clue to mechanism. It may also happen that a product is a reagent which, either fortuitously or in some regulatory role, tends to inactivate one or more forms of the enzyme. Enzymes that catalyze reactions yielding H_2O_2 as one product, for example, are often subject to "reaction inactivation" in test systems. Again, however, the phenomenon is not easily put to systematic use in studying mechanisms.

A more useful situation, especially in multistep mechanisms, is the diminution of overall reaction velocity by a product that ties up the form

---

[5] This is only one special case of the general class of substrate inhibition resulting from combination of the substrate with enzyme to form a "dead end" complex, i.e., a complex than cannot go on to form product.

of the enzyme from which that product is normally discharged. It is apparent, for example, that if the last step of a catalytic sequence is reversible, the last product discharged and the first substrate taken on must compete for the free, uncombined form of the enzyme, whatever the position of equilibrium in the overall reaction. For reactions producing more than one product, the systematic study of initial velocities in the presence of a single product can provide important information about the formal mechanism (9). This usage will be dealt with in more detail in Chaps. 8 and 9, which have to do with kinetic analysis of two-substrate mechanisms.

SUBSTANCES THAT COMBINE WITH MORE THAN ONE COMPONENT

A topic remaining for consideration concerns the effects of substances that can act in more than one of the areas of the diagram in Fig. 7. The most important class of these is that combining action on the free enzyme (region 1) with action on the enzyme-substrate complex (region 3). This is the class containing the "noncompetitive" inhibitors.[6] The kinetic modification that results from this behavior is simply obtained by including both the "competitive" and "uncompetitive" terms derived previously, as the noncompetitive effect is clearly just the sum of the other two effects. Assuming again that (EA) and (EAQ) are involved in equilibria, and labeling the corresponding equilibrium constants with subscripts indicating their regions in Fig. 7, we obtain from Eqs. (17) and (18)

$$v_0 = \frac{VA_0}{K_m(QK_{Q1} + 1) + A_0(QK_{Q3} + 1)} \tag{20}$$

For the special circumstances that $K_{Q1} = K_{Q3}$ (i.e., where binding of A by the enzyme has absolutely no effect on the binding of Q, a completely noncompetitive situation), the equation becomes

$$v_0 = \frac{A_0 V/(QK_Q + 1)}{K_m + A_0} \tag{21}$$

Equation (21) is the equation of a rectangular hyperbola. The slope-intercept forms give straight lines. The K_m is unaltered by the presence of Q; only the apparent V is changed (Fig. 12). This is the

---

[6] This must *not* be taken to imply that true noncompetitive behavior occurs in all mechanisms only where there is combination with two forms. In multisubstrate mechanisms, noncompetitive behavior commonly results from combination with a single form (see Chap. 7).

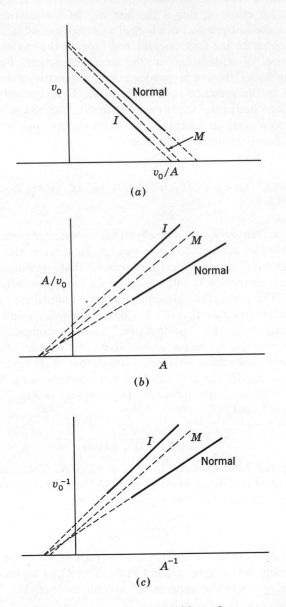

FIG. 12. Noncompetitive and mixed inhibition. *I*, pure noncompetitive inhibition; *M*, mixed inhibition.

kinetic behavior usually taken as diagnostic for simple noncompetitive behavior. It is sometimes envisioned in terms of a conformational change of the enzyme when it is combined with Q, in such a way that it fails to convert A to products.[7] Testing strict conformity to the equations and evaluating the inhibitor constants (K_Q) for both competitive and noncompetitive inhibitors is sometimes done by the graphical method suggested by Dixon (10), as shown in Fig. 13. Plotting V^{-1} or K_m/V against Q can yield the same information.

Obviously, the very special conditions used in this derivation (equilibrium, coincidence of K_{Q1} and K_{Q3}, implying a total functional separation of attachment sites and catalytic sites) will not often be met. The result is that pure noncompetitive behavior is rare. Much of the inhibition observed experimentally has a "mixed" quality, in which both the apparent K_m and the apparent V vary with the concentration of Q (Fig. 12).[8] It follows from this consideration and those mentioned previously that analysis of inhibitory behavior is sometimes a complex business, often requiring for its interpretation considerable detailed prior knowledge of the enzyme mechanism involved. At the minimum, it is necessary to examine the kinetic behavior over as broad a concentration range of inhibitor and of substrate as possible, preferably for both forward and reverse reactions. Direct testing of the effects of the inhibitor on the free substrate must be done using a method that can distinguish the free from the combined substrate.[9] Nevertheless, the rewards of inhibitor analysis, properly done, may be substantial and it has much use in multisubstrate kinetic studies.

As physical methods for detecting conformation changes are further developed, it will also be of importance to examine directly the effects of inhibitors on the enzymes themselves. Even at present in the relatively few cases in which it is possible to examine enzymes in stoichiometric concentrations with their substrates, it should be possible to make quite direct tests of inhibitor effects. In these ways some of the more obvious pitfalls of inhibitor analysis may be avoided.

Table 2 summarizes the kinetic appearance of inhibition caused by combination with the various components of the catalytic reaction scheme.

---

[7] Note again that superficially similar behavior could be given by either an irreversible Q (enzyme inactivation) or by combined action on the *substrate* and enzyme-substrate complex.

[8] Some kineticists prefer to call "noncompetitive" any inhibition in which both the slop (K_m/V) and intercept $(1/V)$ of the double reciprocal plot are altered.

[9] Not, e.g., a tritrimetric method, which could not distinguish free substrate from substrate bound in a mobile equilibrium.

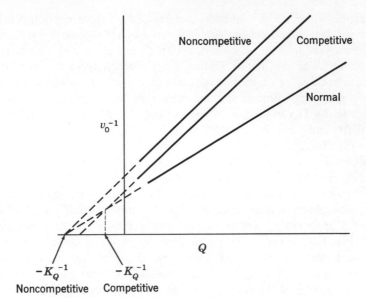

FIG. 13.   Determination of K_Q by Dixon's method.

TABLE 2.   *Apparent Kinetic Behavior of Modifiers*

Site of action	Reversibility	
	Reversible	Irreversible
E^a	Competitive, Eq. (17)	NC[b] (Fig. 8)
A	Competitive, Eq. (17A)	Nonlinear (Fig. 9)
(EA)	Uncompetitive, Eq. (18)	NC
(EA) + E	Noncompetitive, Eq. (20)	NC
(EA) + A	Noncompetitive, Eq. (20)	NC

[a] The symbols used refer to the components of Fig. 7.

[b] NC refers to behavior yielding plots that look noncompetitive. Secondary plots of slopes and intercepts of double reciprocal plots against modifier concentration are not linear, however, as they must be for reversible inhibition.

ACTIVATION

Thus far we have considered only cases in which Q is an inhibitor. Suppose, however, that (EAQ) of Fig. 7, whether formed from $(EQ) + A$, from $(AQ) + E$ or from $(EA) + Q$, can decompose to $E + X + Q$ more rapidly than (EA) can decompose to $E + X$.[10] That is, we now wish to abandon our special requirement that the Q-containing intermediates are dead ends.

The equations are the same as in the noncompetitive case just discussed except that in this case the total velocity is a sum of the velocities (v_0 and v_0') obtained by decomposition of (EA), given by Eq. (20), and of (EAQ), given by $E_0' = k_{+2}'(EAQ)$. The latter term can be obtained by reference to conditions of Q saturation (i.e., at such high Q concentration that the velocity does not change significantly when Q is further increased). Under these conditions it is easily shown that the velocity expression is

$$v_0^{\text{total}} \text{ at } Q_{\text{sat}} = \frac{k_{+2}' K_{Q3} A_0 E_0}{K_m K_{Q1} + K_{Q3} A_0} \tag{22}$$

A slope-intercept form of Eq. (22) is

$$\frac{v_0}{A_0} = -\frac{v_0 K_{Q3}}{K_m K_{Q1}} + \frac{k_{+2}' K_{Q3} E_0}{K_m K_{Q1}}$$

Thus a plot of v_0/A_0 against v_0 will give $-K_{Q3}/K_m K_{Q1}$ as slope and $k_{+2}' E_0$ as intercept on the v_0 axis. Since K_m can be evaluated from work in the absence of Q, the ratio of the K_Q constants can be obtained. Clearly, the ratio corresponding to the true noncompetitive situation is unity.

Finally, it must be stressed that the derivations given here have been done under the simplifying assumption that the breakdown reactions of (EA) and (EAQ) are so slow that they do not significantly disturb the equilibria among the various free and combined forms appearing in these mechanisms. A full steady-state treatment of these noncompetitive situations is so complex as to be unmanageable for practical purposes. Morales (11) has shown, however, that the strict applicability of the equations here given (i.e., pure noncompetitive behavior) is only to the equilibrium case. Indeed, strict conformity to this behavior has been taken as evidence that equilibrium conditions do obtain. The only other cause of typical noncompetitive behavior would be blockage of one of the alternate reaction pathways leading to (EAQ).[11]

---

[10] What follows also applies to the case where (EAQ) decomposes to product more slowly than does (EA) but still at a significant rate. The case in which both complexes decompose at the same rate is trivial, as no effect of Q is then discernible.

[11] This is related to the general rule, to be discussed later, that any mechanism in which a substrate reacts at significant velocity with more than one enzymic form (in this case E and EQ) in pathways leading to product gives rise to atypical kinetics (e.g., non-linear reciprocal plots) unless equilibrium conditions obtain.

EFFECTS OF pH

All of the above considerations apply when the hydronium ion is considered as inhibitor or activator. Here the assumption of equilibrium conditions in the inhibition or activation reactions is likely to be a good one, as ionic reactions involving the hydronium ion are particularly fast. Since in general, however, we must consider both protonation and deprotonation of any form as potentially significant for activity, the modified diagram shown in Fig. 14 will serve as the basis for development. The derivation is shown in full below. The student should be able to follow it readily at this point. For convenience we shall omit the ionizations of the substrate, as they can be known independently.

Equilibria:

$$k_{+a}(EH) = k_{-a}HE \qquad \text{or} \qquad E = \frac{(EH)}{H}K_a \qquad (23)$$

$$k_{+b}H(EH) = k_{-b}(EH_2) \qquad \text{or} \qquad (EH_2) = H(EH)K_b \qquad (24)$$

$$k_{+c}(EHA) = k_{-c}H(EA) \qquad \text{or} \qquad (EA) = \frac{(EHA)}{H}K_c \qquad (25)$$

$$k_{+d}H(EHA) = k_{-d}(EH_2 A) \qquad \text{or} \qquad (EH_2 A) = H(EHA)K_d \qquad (26)$$

The steady state:

$$k_{+1}A(EH) + k_{-d}(EH_2 A) + k_{-c}H(EA) = (EHA)(k_{-1} + k_{+2} + k_{+c} + k_{+d}H) \qquad (27)$$

Combining

$$(EHA) = \frac{A(EH)}{K_m} \qquad \text{or} \qquad (EH) = \frac{K_m(EHA)}{A} \qquad (28)$$

Conservation equation for enzyme:

$$E_0 = E + (EH) + (EH_2) + (EA) + (EHA) + (EH_2 A) \qquad (29)$$

Combining with equilibrium equations and Eq. (28),

$$E_0 = (EHA)\left[\frac{K_m}{A}\left(1 + \frac{K_a}{H} + HK_b\right) + 1 + \frac{K_c}{H} + HK_d\right] \qquad (30)$$

And, since $v_0 = k_{+2}(EHA)$,

$$v_0 = \frac{k_{+2}E_0 A}{K_m\left(1 + \frac{K_a}{H} + HK_b\right) + A\left(1 + \frac{K_c}{H} + HK_d\right)} \qquad (31)$$

Consider, then, the alkaline pH range, i.e., the range in which only equilibria a and c are active. Suppose, further that $K_a = K_c$, i.e., that substrate attachment does not alter the pK of the group involved.

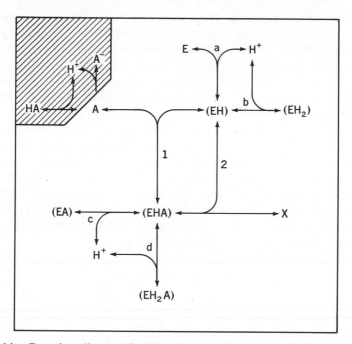

FIG. 14. Reaction diagram for H^+ as a modifier. The symbols are to be understood in a very general sense. The symbol (EH) represents all those forms of the enzyme that can combine with A; (EHA) represents all forms that can go on to yield product X, etc. In other words, only those ionizations relating to the activity are considered. The shaded area refers to the fact that ionizations of the substrate, while important kinetically, can be known independently and thus are not included in the derivation given in the text.

Then Eq. (31) becomes

$$v_0 = \frac{k_{+2} E_0 A}{(K_m + A)\left(1 + \frac{K_a}{H}\right)} \quad \text{or} \quad v_0 = \frac{AV \Big/ \left(1 + \frac{K_a}{H}\right)}{K_m + A} \tag{32}$$

Similarly, on the acid side, where only K_b and K_d are significant *and* for the circumstance that $K_b = K_d$:

$$v_0 = \frac{k_{+2} E_0 A}{(K_m + A)(1 + HK_b)} \quad \text{or} \quad v_0 = \frac{AV/(1 + HK_b)}{K_m + A} \tag{33}$$

Notice that for these special cases, where substrate binding does not affect the K, that the *shape* of the curve v_0 against pH is not affected by A, whereas in the general case (Eq. 31) the shape must be dependent on substrate concentration.

Clearly, for either pH range considered separately this analysis is exactly analogous to the noncompetitive development for modifiers in general. It should also be noted that pure noncompetitive pH behavior, like pure noncompetitive behavior in general, will be relatively rare, occurring only when equilibrium conditions in enzyme substrate complex formation are met.[12] Moreover, circumstances like those yielding competitive modifier effects in the general case (i.e., proton dissociation reactions involving either free enzyme or free substrate only) will yield competitive pH effects. K_m will be altered, but not V. Similarly, effects involving only the enzyme-substrate complex will alter both K_m and V, in "uncompetitive" proportion, so that the velocity at very low substrate concentrations is not altered. This behavior is of course a consequence of the fact that at substrate concentrations far below K_m the concentration of EA is vanishingly small and uncompetitive inhibitors have nothing with which to react. Note that

$$v_0 = \frac{k_{+2}}{K_m} E_0 A = \frac{V}{K_m} A$$

where the denominator term involving the uncompetitive inhibitor constant [Eq. (18)] is no longer significant.

Some convenient plotting forms for dealing with the variation of K_m, V and V/K_m with pH for purposes of detecting significant catalytic groups in enzymes are given in Chap. 14.

GENERAL REFERENCES

Laidler, K. J.: *The Chemical Kinetics of Enzyme Action*, Oxford, London, 1958.
Dixon, M., and E. C. Webb: *Enzymes*, 2nd ed., Academic, New York, 1964.
Reiner, J. M.: *Behavior of Enzyme Systems*, Burgess, Minneapolis, 1959.
Webb, J. L.: *Enzyme and Metabolic Inhibitors*, Academic, New York, 1963.

[12] Laidler has made a completely detailed analysis of these reactions, in which he takes account of the possibilities for forming $EH_2 A$ from $EH_2 + A$, etc., and proceeds by full-fledged steady-state treatment rather than assuming equilibrium in the ionizations (12). He showed that there are actually only two circumstances under which Eq. (32) is rigorously correct for a noncompetitive occurrence. These are (a) where $k_{+2} \ll k_{-1}$, i.e., when equilibrium obtains in substrate binding, or (b) when *both* substrate binding and substrate dissociation in one of the available routes is much more rapid than in the others, a condition he considers improbable. Alberty and Bloomfield (13) have also considered the behavior of the system in which reactions of all three ionized forms of the enzyme occur as significant contributions to the velocity.

SPECIFIC REFERENCES

1. Huang, H. T., and C. Niemann: *J. Am. Chem. Soc.*, **74**: 59 (1952).
2. Rapp, J. R., C. Neimann, and G. E. Hein: *Biochemistry*, **5**: 4100 (1966).
3. Mintel, R., and J. Westley: *J. Biol. Chem.*, **241**: 3381 (1966).
4. Jencks, W. P.: in N. O. Kaplan and E. P. Kennedy (eds.), *Current Aspects of Biochemical Energetics*, Academic, New York, 1966, p. 273.
5. Laidler, K. J.: *The Chemical Kinetics of Enzyme Action*, Oxford, London, 1958, pp. 72–77.
6. Reiner, J. M.: *Behavior of Enzyme Systems*, Burgess, Minneapolis, 1959, pp. 189–200.
7. Webb, J. L.: *Enzyme and Metabolic Inhibitors*, Academic, New York, 1963, pp. 118–130.
8. Walter, C., and E. Frieden: *Advan. Enzymol.*, **25**: 167 (1963).
9. Cleland, W. W.: *Biochim. et Biophys. Acta*, **67**: 173 (1963).
10. Dixon, M.: *Biochem. J.*, **55**: 170 (1953).
11. Morales, M. F.: *J. Am. Chem. Soc.*, **77**: 4169 (1955).
12. Laidler, K. J.: *Trans. Faraday Soc.*, **51**: 528 (1955).
13. Alberty, R. A., and V. Bloomfield: *J. Biol. Chem.*, **238**: 2804 (1963).

5

SUBSTRATE SPECIFICITY

The concept of enzymic substrate specificity is a further natural consequence of the effort to understand the phenomena involved in enzyme-substrate complex formation and inhibition. It is inevitable that two enzymes catalyzing different types of reactions, say hydrolysis and dehydrogenation, should show a differential selectivity among substrates on the basis of the functional groups present. Moreover, unless the attachment of a substrate is invariably by a single group only and unless attachment is invariably the only necessary component in the catalysis, there must also be some degree of steric specificity. Even if these unlikely conditions obtained, selectivity on a geometrical basis would still be expected for mechanisms involving the formation of ternary complexes between the enzyme and two substrates.

COMPLEX FORMATION AND BOND CLEAVAGE

These considerations are easily appreciated when we try to envision in detail the probable events in an enzyme-catalyzed reaction. The substrate must first attach to the enzyme. Because of the great difference in size, in general, the substrate is in contact with a very limited portion of the enzyme molecule. It is this consideration that has given rise to the concept of the active sites of enzymes. Of course, the active site need not be (and probably very rarely if ever is) a short consecutive region in the primary structure of the enzyme. It is instead a localized portion of the array presented in the fully folded globular structure of the enzyme molecule in solution. Attachment of the substrate is on the basis of the weak forces considered in Chap. 3, which involve interactions between particular groups, or at least particular kinds of groups, in the enzyme and substrate. If the attachment is polyfunctional, with the binding force including significant contributions from interactions of more than one pair of groups, it is obvious that the spacings of the critical groups in the active site and the substrate must be in some way matched. The fact that protein structure is to some extent mobile does not fundamentally alter this fact, although it does provide somewhat more latitude for the complementarity. Potential substrates having the required groupings arrayed "incorrectly" will then not attach well, an effect on k_{-1}/k_{+1} in kinetic terms, which may or may not be reflected in an abnormally large K_m but is not in any case evident in V.

Following complex formation in a one-substrate reaction is the k_{+2} step. To take a concrete example, this may be the rupture of a bond in the substrate. If a group in the active site other than a substrate binding group is involved in the electronic displacement resulting in bond rupture, that group must also be properly juxtaposed relative to the bound substrate. Otherwise the electronic displacement does not occur efficiently and k_{+2} is diminished. This effect thus appears directly in V and also affects K_m to the extent that k_{+2} is a significant term in the K_m.

In the case of two-substrate reactions involving ternary complexes, it is evident that the two substrates must be juxtaposed in a way permitting the reaction. It is difficult to envision any mechanism for reactions involving direct transfer of an atom or group between two substrates if the molecules in question are not bound at spatially adjacent or overlapping sites. Therefore, in this case as in the ones preceding, the precise arrays of substrate groups and enzymic binding groups might be expected to be of great importance.

It follows from these considerations that, in addition to the group specificity involving a requirement for a certain reactive grouping in the substrate molecule, an enzyme might commonly be expected to display at least some degree of steric specificity. It would further be anticipated that steric specificity could in general affect any or all of the kinetic coefficients.

It should be noted in connection with this discussion that enzyme-substrate complexes may undergo unimolecular isomerizations such that there are in fact many sequential intermediates rather than just one. Peller and Alberty (1) have analyzed the kinetic consequences of such a phenomenon. Their results indicate that the kinetic forms are the same as for single intermediates, but the rate constants evaluated on the assumption of a single intermediate will indicate only the lower limits of the true rate constants.

ASYMMETRIC REACTIONS OF SYMMETRICAL SUBSTRATES

An interesting further extension of steric specificity arises for the case of substrate molecules that have elements of symmetry but are nonetheless treated asymmetrically in enzymic reactions. *Meso* carbon atoms, for example, are treated by enzymes as if they were asymmetric structures. This is the situation with citrate, a case in which Ogston first pointed out that a three-point attachment of substrate to enzyme could provide the basis for the asymmetric reaction (2). Actually, two specific points of attachment are all that is required to orient the substrate group to be reacted in a stereospecific way. In the schematic representation in Fig. 15 the substrate itself possesses a plane of symmetry and is attached by only the two groups A and B; yet the enzyme-substrate complex depicted is clearly asymmetric. Substrate groups C and C', although identical, can certainly be expected to display different reactivities with respect to other bound molecules, enzymic groups, or free solute or solvent molecules present. The important feature of this system is of course the asymmetry of the enzyme, formulated in this case in terms of noninterchangeable sites for A and B and a non-uniformity in properties in the dimension perpendicular to the enzyme surface.

An example easily understood in terms of the diagram in Fig. 15 is the substrate specificity of yeast alcohol dehydrogenase, which has been documented in terms of K_m values and maximum velocities for ethyl, methyl, and isopropyl alcohols (3). If groups C and C' of Fig. 15 are envisioned as the hydrogen atoms of the *meso* carbon of ethanol, A and B are the hydroxyl and methyl groups. Replacement of the methyl group by a hydrogen atom (methanol) caused a twenty-fivefold decrease in maximum velocity and a sixty-fivefold increase in K_m. Furthermore, replacement of a hydrogen atom on the *meso* carbon by a methyl group (isopropyl alcohol) caused a two and one-halffold decrease in maximum velocity and a seventyfold increase in K_m. The implication was that a combination of both these replacements, which would be achieved if enthanol were inserted into the active site "backwards," would surely have very large effects on the activity.[1] Other evidence shows that this is indeed the case, as the enzyme displays

[1] The velocity at low alcohol concentration would be equal to V/K_m times that concentration. Taking V/K_m as the measure of velocity, then, yields factors of 155 between the velocities with ethyl and methyl alcohols and 1700 between those with ethyl and isopropyl alcohols. This suggests a possible velocity factor in excess of 10^5 between the two orientations of ethanol.

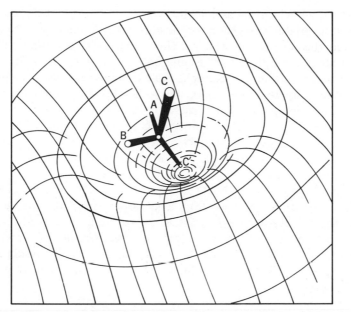

FIG. 15. Perspective view of a surface with a concavity in which a tetra-hedral molecule with groups ABC and C' is bound.

absolute stereospecificity for orientation of the alcohol, and has even been used to prepare optically active monodeutero ethanol (3).

OTHER EXAMPLES

The foregoing expectations are amply fulfilled by the results of specificity studies with many enzymes. A number of enzymes display only very broad group specificities. The alkaline phosphatase of *E. coli*, for example, catalyzes the hydrolysis of a great variety of phosphoric esters, apparently without a marked selectivity among these substrates (4). In this case it seems probable that the formation of the enzyme-phosphoric ester complex is primarily an ionic interaction, since all of the esters are anionic and Zn^{2+} is known to be an essential component of the active site of this enzyme.

Most enzymes, however, show higher degrees of specificity. Some are absolutely specific for one substrate (or one pair of substrates) out of all of the many tested. The higher degrees of specificity include, notably, strict stereospecificity. For example, in enzyme-catalyzed reactions in which an asymmetric center is formed, the product is almost invariably a single one of the possible enantiomorphs. It follows that in the reversal of such reactions, and quite generally where a substrate is optically active, usually only one of the enantiomorphs is active as a substrate. For example, yeast contains separate L-lactate and D-lactate dehydrogenases (5,6). The other optical isomer may be a competitive inhibitor in such cases (7).

The most extensively documented case of enzymic stereospecificity is that involving the pyridine nucleotide coenzymes. Vennesland and her co-workers have used isotopic methods to demonstrate that the hydrogen atom added to the 4 position of the pyridine ring in the enzyme-catalyzed reduction of NAD occupies exclusively one of the two possible positions in space (8).[2] The carbon atom that accepts the hydrogen is not asymmetric in either the oxidized or reduced forms of the coenzyme, but enzymes catalyze the direct transfer of a hydrogen atom from a substrate molecule to just one side of the pyridine ring at that position. Some enzymes are specific for one side of the ring, some for the other.

Another well-established case of stereospecificity of this sort is in the enzymic phosphorylation of glycerol (9). Glycerol is certainly not an asymmetric compound but it is handled asymmetrically by its kinase. The enzyme catalyzes esterification of one of the two primary alcohol groups exclusively, yielding only one of the enantiomorphic α-glycerol phosphoric esters as product, L-α-glycerol phosphate. The key event, again, is the formation of an asymmetric enzyme-substrate complex. The presence of a *meso* carbon atom in the substrate is only what enables us to see the asymmetry of the resulting synthesis.

Again at this point, as in earlier (and later) chapters, attention must be called to the highly detailed structures of enzymes and enzyme-substrate complexes inferred from X-ray crystallographic data. As more data are accumulated to indicate the relationships between molecular structure in the crystals and that in solution, these may well become our most fruitful source of mechanistic information. There is already in the literature some evidence regarding enzymic activity in the crystal state (10–12). It is noteworthy that all of the crystallographic pictures indicate "clefts" or "pockets" for substrate binding, in accord with previous ideas on stereospecificity.

---

[2] These are studies in the same series as the widely discussed experiments that demonstrated direct transfer of hydrogen atoms from substrates to the coenzymes, referred to in Chap. 3.

SPECIFICITY APPLICATIONS IN MECHANISM WORK

The stereospecific behavior of a number of other metabolic re-actions has been considered as evidence relating to the formal mechan-isms of catalysis. For example, the constancy of stereochemical specificity in a series of keto aldehyde isomerases has led Rose (13) to propose a common *cis*-endiol mechanism for these four enzymes and to suggest that the bonds involved in each case may be cleaved by a concerted mechanism. In contrast, the opposite stereochemical properties of the otherwise very similar glutamate mutase and methylmalonyl coenzyme A (CoA) mutase have been taken to indicate that the inter-change of hydrogen atoms and substituent groups in the substrates probably occurs by at least two independent steps rather than by a concerted mechanism (14).

Meister (15) has made an elegant application of substrate specificity studies to the inference of spatial array in the active site of glutamine synthetase. The stereospecificity of this enzyme is peculiar in that it utilizes both D- and L-glutamate but only the D isomer of β-glutamate and only the L isomer of α-methylglutamate. These observations led to a highly specific rationale in terms of spatial arrays of substrate groups and the complementary array in the active site. Predictions based on this rationale have been borne out in further studies with variously substituted substrates.

The foregoing studies suggest that we may be seeing much more research utilizing enzyme specificity in the analysis of mechanisms. As a matter of fact, several illustrations of the many uses of alternate substrates are recounted in Part II of this book.

In general, it is usual to emphasize the extremely strict specificity of which enzymes are capable. Granting this point, especially as regards absolute stereospecificity at the reaction center, it seems useful to go on to place emphasis on the fact that enzymes may have practically any degree or kind of specificity. An interesting, and somewhat corrective, case in point is the comparison made by Pocker and Meany (16) of the enzymic and metal ion-catalyzed hydrations of pyridine aldehydes. In this study, free divalent zinc or cobalt ions showed a marked specificity (several hundredfold) for 2-pyridine aldehyde over 4-pyridine aldehyde, evidently on a steric basis. For example, the specificity could be related

to the dimensions of —$\overset{|}{\underset{|}{Zn}}$—OH as a bifunctional catalyst. In contrast, the zinc-containing enzyme carbonic anhydrase, which is a highly efficient catalyst for the same reaction, showed no specificity distinction between these two substrates. Such an instance where an enzyme has *less* specificity than other common catalysts, indicates clearly that the only valid sweeping generalization on enzyme specificity may be a comment on versatility. In view of the critical roles of specificity in enzyme catalytic theory (Chap. 6), however, this comment may well be worth making.

GENERAL REFERENCES

Levy, H. R., P. Talalay, and B. Vennesland: in P. B. D. de la Mare and W. Klyne (eds.), *Progress in Stereochemistry*, Vol. 3, Butterworths, London, 1962.
Rose, I. A.: *Ann. Rev. Biochem.*, **35**: (1966).
Jencks, W. P.: in N. O. Kaplan and E. P. Kennedy (eds.), *Current Aspects of Biochemical Energetics*, Academic, New York, 1966.
Gutfreund, H.: in P. D. Boyer, H. Lardy, and K. Myrbäck (eds.), *The Enzymes*, 2nd ed., Vol. 1, 1959.

SPECIFIC REFERENCES

1. Peller, L., and R. A. Alberty: *J. Am. Chem. Soc.*, **81**: 5907 (1959).
2. Ogston, A. G.: *Nature*, **164**: 180 (1949).
3. Levy, H. R., F. A. Loewus, and B. Vennesland: *J. Am. Chem. Soc.*, **79**: 2949 (1957).
4. Heppel, L. A., D. R. Harkness, and R. J. Hilmoe: *J. Biol. Chem.*, **237**: 841 (1962).
5. Back, S. J., M. Dixon, and L. G. Zerfas: *Biochem. J.*, **40**: 229 (1946).
6. Nygaard, A. P.: *J. Biol. Chem.*, **236**: 920 (1961).
7. Huang, H. T., and C. Niemann: *J. Am. Chem. Soc.*, **73**: 1555 (1951).
8. Vennesland, B.: *J. Cellular Comp. Physiol.*, **47**: 201 (1956).
9. Bublitz, C., and E. P. Kennedy: *J. Biol. Chem.*, **211**: 963 (1955).
10. Richards, F. M.: *Brookhaven Symp. Biol.*, **15**: 208 (1962).
11. Murdock, A. L.: *Federation Proc.*, **26**: 385 (1967).
12. Quiocho, F. A., W. H. Bishop, and F. M. Richards: *Proc. Natl. Acad. Sci. U.S.*, **57**: 525 (1967).
13. Rose, I. A.: *Brookhaven Symp. Biol.*, **15**: 293 (1962).
14. Sprecher, M., M. J. Clark, and D. B. Sprinson: *J. Biol. Chem.*, **241**: 872 (1966).
15. Meister, A.: *Federation Proc.*, **27**: 100 (1968).
16. Pocker, Y., and J. E. Meany: *J. Am. Chem. Soc.*, **89**: 631 (1967).

6

THEORIES OF ENZYME ACTION

In rounding out our account of fundamentals in enzymology, we need to consider some of the ideas that have been expressed relating enzyme action to theories of catalysis. Fundamentally, of course, enzymes alter the free energies of activation of the reactions they catalyze. It is not obvious a priori, however, whether the effects are primarily on the enthalpies or the entropies of activation. Nevertheless, with the results of a large volume of experimental work as a guide, there have been several fruitful discussions of the possible causes contributing to enzymic catalysis. Seven major factors are discernible. We shall describe these factors briefly and then illustrate their application to what is very likely the best understood enzyme-catalyzed reaction, that of α-chymotrypsin.

JUXTAPOSITION AND ORIENTATION

It is intriguing to consider the possibility that enzymes might be nothing more than surfaces where substrates that are to interact sit down together. At the enzyme surface the substrates are present at high concentrations even when the bulk solution contains only very low concentrations of substrates. The distinction to be made is clearly akin to the distinction between inter- and intramolecular reactions. Koshland has investigated this possibility, including also the question of the proper orientation of the substrates to each other (1,2). The calculations made were of course based on approximations but the values obtained should certainly be useful in an orders-of-magnitude way. The conclusions were that simple approximation and orientation of substrates to each other could not possibly account for enzymic catalysis. The discrepancy was many orders of magnitude. It was only when he considered both the juxtaposition and orientation of the substrates to each other and also to catalytic groups in the enzyme that Koshland found large increases in rate to be expected theoretically.

As an *empirical* generalization, the contribution of pure juxta-position effects has been recognized as expressible in the following terms: the velocity of a simple intramolecular interaction may be taken as approximately equal to the velocity of the corresponding bimolecular reaction where one of the reactants is present at 10 M concentration (2–4). The number does not have an obvious physical rationale but represents only a kind of orders-of-magnitude summary of experience in comparing the velocity of reaction between groups on separate molecules with that of reaction between the same groups attached to the same molecule. This must be recognized as a very gross approximation. Perhaps the earlier formulation (5) of such a factor as the elimination of "unmixing" is to be preferred.[1]

CHANGE OF REACTING SPECIES

In cases in which the enzyme reacts with the substrates sequentially, accepting a group from one substrate, say, and transferring it to another, a very simple possibility exists for lowering the free energy of activation by changing the entire character of the reaction. For example, where the final acceptor substrate is not very reactive in the kinetic sense, a more reactive enzymic group may make the attack on the donor substrate, cleaving it with formation of a reactive substituted enzyme. This appears to be a major factor in the action of many hydrolases, where the attack is made by an excellent nucleophile such as $-O^-$, as in chymotrypsin (see below), or $-S^-$, as in papain (7). In a formally similar way, where the two substrates are ions of like charge,[2] their spontaneous reaction is severely limited by the electrostatic hindrance to approach of the reacting species. In such cases, reaction of the enzyme with the donor substrate, either with discharge of an anionic first product or with neutralization of charge by a cationic group of the enzyme, would be expected to contribute substantially to increased reaction velocity. The sulfur transferase rhodanese provides a simple example of this effect. Here the spontaneous reaction of the substrates SSO_3^{2-} and CN^-

---

[1] "Unmixing" refers to the probability matter of sorting out solute molecules from the solvent. It gives rise to an entropy of activation term of about -8 e.u. in all bimolecular reactions (5). Allowance for bimolecularity on this basis is equivalent to assumption of about a 50 M (rather than a 10 M) concentration of second reactant (6).

[2] Very many substrates, for example, are phosphoric anions.

is electrostatically hindered. The enzyme, however, reacts with SSO_3^{2-}, accepting neutral sulfur and discharging SO_3^{2-} (8,9). The subsequent approach of CN^- to the transferable sulfur atom is then entirely unhindered electrostatically. The reaction has been transformed so that it does not involve an anion–anion interaction at any point. It will be noted that if this electrostatic factor is really significant, the thiosulfate-cyanide reaction should also be catalyzed to some extent by anion-exchange resins. This prediction is fulfilled, the degree of catalysis, however, being very much less than that of the enzyme (10). This kind of contribution to catalysis is capable of generalization to include many kinds of changes in the character of the reaction.

ELECTRONIC EFFECTS

There has been much more discussion of the catalytic factors that may be grouped as electronic effects since they involve an electronic displacement in a substrate occasioned by the approach of nucleophilic or electrophilic, or both, groups of the enzyme. These are perhaps most easily understood in terms of simple model catalysts. For example, imidazole catalyzes ester hydrolytic reactions, which are in fact acyl transfer reactions, involving the formation of acylimidazole intermediates. This catalysis clearly involves nucleophilic attack of the imidazole upon the ester carbonyl carbon, resulting in the formation of

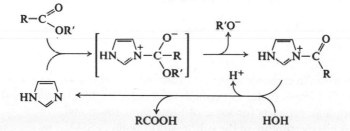

the unstable acyl imidazole. This is of course an intriguing model system, especially since imidazole groups have been implicated in the action of many enzymes. Nevertheless, no acyl enzyme intermediates have been demonstrated in which the acyl group resides on an imidazole.

The fact is that the acyl enzymes demonstrated for the peptidases and esterases are probably all intermediates in which the acyl group is esterified to either a serine hydroxyl group or a sulfhydryl group. This finding is not really surprising since both the serine hydroxyl anion and the sulfhydryl anion are excellent nucleophiles. Because it is precisely these enzymes, however, which seem on other grounds to have imidazole groups in their active sites, some other mechanism of imidazole involvement is required. This mechanism apparently involves general-acid-base catalysis, as discussed in the next section of this chapter.

Catalysis by electrophilic groups of the enzyme may perhaps be most easily understood in terms of metal ion catalysis as a model. Clearly, metal ions can accommodate electrons. Accordingly, the approach of a substrate to a metal ion, be it a "free" (actually solvent-coordinated) ion or one coordinated to enzymic groups, can be expected to result in a qualitatively predictable electronic displacement in the substrate. Thus the need for a metal ion in the enolase reaction is rationalized in terms of the relatively easy departure of the hydroxyl group from 2-phosphoglycerate when it is associated with an electrophilic group (11,12).

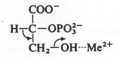

The role of the enzymic zinc ion in the action of carboxypeptidase appears to have a similar basis (13). Here the metal ion serves to polarize the peptide carbonyl group of the substrate, facilitating attack by an enzymic nucleophile.

The zinc ion in carbonic anydrase presumably functions in a very similar way (14). Simple metal ion complexes (and even hydronium ions) are electrophilic catalysts for some of these same reactions.

Similarly, rupture of the sulfur–sulfur bond in SSO_3^{2-} by rhodanese involves at least in part an electrophilic mechanism. Evidence has been obtained indicating that the substrate thiosulfate, presumably coordinated through its oxygens to an enzymic zinc ion, suffers thereby an electronic displacement that results in bond scission, the outer sulfur atom being transferred to a nucleophilic group in the enzyme (6,15).

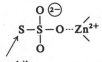

Metzger and Wilson (16) have also obtained convincing evidence for an electrophilic mechanism in catalysis by various hydrolytic enzymes.

GENERAL-ACID-BASE CATALYSIS

Acid-base reactions generally are distinguishable from all other reactions only as long as reasonably restrictive definitions of the terms acid and base are maintained. When we go beyond the Brönsted (17) to the Lewis (18) definitions and especially to the very general treatments (19,20), all nucleophiles become bases and all electrophiles (e.g., metal ions) acids. We shall find it more useful here to restrain our enthusiasm for generality and retain the Brönsted definitions. Thus general-acid catalysis is a rate increase occasioned by the partial transfer of a proton from any Brönsted acid to a reactant in the transition state. Similarly, general-base catalysis occurs when any Brönsted base accelerates a reaction by accepting partial transfer of a proton from a transition state complex. A great many organic and inorganic reactions are known to be catalyzed by such means. To cite just one class of examples, reactions involving rate-limiting formation of enol forms commonly are subject to both general-acid and general-base catalysis.

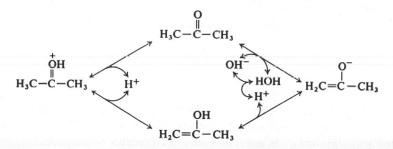

In view of these facts it would be astonishing if enzymes, which have groups ionizable in all parts of the physiologically significant pH range, did not take advantage of the acid-base catalytic mechanisms. Accordingly, much has been written and said about the possible participation of various enzymic groups in this way. It is extremely difficult, however, to demonstrate such participation unequivocally and the success of most enzymic mechanisms involving general-acid-base catalysis is based more on plausibility than on demonstration. Nevertheless, a strong probability for such participation of the imidazole group in particular has been established.

The case for imidazole is based primarily on two kinds of observations: (a) A great deal of experimental work on essential residues has implicated histidine in the activity of many enzymes. (b) In no case does it appear that the imidazole reacts as a nucleophile; e.g., in the acyl enzyme intermediates it is not the histidine that is substituted but most often a serine. These observations practically invite the enzymologist to propose a role for the imidazole as a general-base catalyst, accepting a proton from the serine hydroxyl group to form the strongly nucleophilic —O$^-$. Alternatively, one might cast the imidazolium ion as a general-acid catalyst, to protonate the base released from the split substrate.

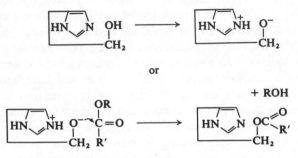

Exactly the same considerations can be used to explain deacylation of the enzyme by water, as we shall see in the section on chymotrypsin.

SOLVENT EFFECTS

Free energies of activation, like free energies generally, are composed of entropy and enthalpy terms. $\Delta G^{\ddagger} = \Delta H^{\ddagger} - T\Delta S^{\ddagger}$. Whereas the enthalpy terms, as expressed in the Arrhenius activation energies, for example, are strongly dependent on formation and cleavage of covalent bonds and reflect van der Waals' forces between the reacting species at close approach in the activated complex, the entropy values contain terms representing a number of mechanistically diverse phenomena. Under this heading must appear electrostriction effects and some other effects of the solvent on the reaction velocity, changes in entropies of reacting substrate molecules, including some of the effects of strain induced in the substrate molecule by attachment to the enzyme, the effects of conformation changes in enzymes occasioned by the binding of substrates, and the "freezing" of the substrate by binding to the enzyme in a conformation resembling that of the activated state for the reaction catalyzed. Not all of these possible contributions are distinguishable experimentally at present, but they are distinct in principle and warrant close examination, as the catalytic contribution involved can amount to changes in rate constants by several orders of magnitude.

In practice, it is possible to separate the electrostatic and non-electrostatic contributions to the entropy of activation by combining two experimental approaches. As discussed in more detail in Chap. 13, the overall entropy of activation $(\Delta S^{\ddagger})$ can be obtained for an individual reaction from measurements of the rate constant at different temperatures. The same approach can be used to obtain $\Delta S^{\ddagger}$ for a single step in an enzyme-catalyzed reaction when it can be shown that the same step is being measured at all the temperatures used.

The electrostatic contribution $(\Delta S^{\ddagger}_{es})$ can be determined from the effect of variations in either ionic strength or dielectric constant, as shown in Chap. 13. Under conditions where the Debye–Hückel limiting law applies, plots of $\log k$ against the square root of the ionic strength yield straight lines with slopes equal to $Z_A Z_B$, the product of ionic charges either brought together or separated in the reaction. Clearly, where there is no electrostatic interaction, one or both of the Z terms is zero and there is no effect of ionic strength. Similarly, where the dielectric constant of the medium can be varied, a plot of $\log k_0$ (the rate constant extrapolated to zero ionic strength) against the inverse dielectric constant yields a slope term permitting evaluation of $Z_A Z_B$. Once this product is known, by either method of measurement, $\Delta S^{\ddagger}_{es}$ can be calculated approximately, assuming a reasonable figure for the closeness of approach of the charge centers. Thus for aqueous solutions at room temperature, and assuming an approach to 2 Å, $\Delta S^{\ddagger}_{es} \simeq 10 Z_A Z_B$.

The interpretation of $\Delta S^{\ddagger}_{es}$ is usually in terms of electrostriction effects, i.e., the binding or freeing of water attendant upon charge separation or charge neutralization, respectively, in ionic reactions. The values obtained by the means given above are approximate, especially so in view of the assumptions required in applying this treatment to proteins (see Chap. 13), but nonetheless are quite useful in making the essentially qualitative distinction regarding the occurrence of a major nonelectrostatic contribution to $\Delta S^{\ddagger}$, which is obtained by difference: $\Delta S^{\ddagger}_{nes} = \Delta S^{\ddagger} - \Delta S^{\ddagger}_{es}$.

The nonelectrostatic contribution is itself complex, containing many possible contributions, but only a single one of these may ordinarily be separated. This is the entropy of "unmixing" (mentioned above in connection with juxtaposition effects), which is an entropy loss of about 8 entropy units occurring whenever a single complex is made from two separate particles, entirely aside from the effects of any accompanying changes. The remaining nonelectrostatic contributions are considered below in connection with conformation changes.

A further "solvent effect" seems not to have received much explicit attention. This concerns the finding that those enzymes that have been examined closely have distinctly nonpolar active site regions. This may well be a critical factor in enzymic catalysis, amounting to the opportunity to do nonaqueous chemistry in aqueous solution. Horecker (21) has commented on the advantage such an environment confers on the aldolases, which must eliminate a molecule of water to form a Schiff base intermediate, but as yet there seems to have been no quantitative treatment of such matters.

CHANGES IN CONFORMATION OF ENZYME AND SUBSTRATE, EFFECTS OF STRAIN

Many enzymic reactions have steps for which $\Delta S^{\ddagger}_{nes}$ is far beyond what can be explained on electrostatic or simple mixing–unmixing bases. For example, the $\Delta S^{\ddagger}$ for the deacylation of acetyl-α-chymotrypsin is about -36 entropy units (22). Such effects are consistent with several alternative explanations, which have not as yet been distinguished experimentally. One possibility is that the enzyme undergoes a conformation change (23). Such an effect is involved in the "induced fit" hypothesis of Koshland (24), which proposes that conformation changes occurring in enzymes on complexing with their substrates are responsible for the positioning of catalytic groups. As pointed out by Bender et al. (22), the "induced fit" could give rise to large entropy of activation effects not readily predictable (as to magnitude) from the structures of the substrates. Further good quantitative measurements of activation entropies may permit distinction of this possibility from the others discussed below. In this same connection, notice should be taken of Hammes' proposal (25) that changes occurring in enzyme tertiary structure on complex formation may contribute to the catalysis by providing compensating energetic changes to balance in part the energy of activation requirements for reacting substrates.

A second possibility is that the bonds in the substrate are subjected to strain by attachment of the substrate to the enzyme either in terms of a rigid or a mobile enzyme structure (26–29). This suggestion proceeds most convincingly from the observation that enzyme specificity involves both the binding and the reaction of substrates. As discussed very well by Jencks (29), this possibility does not necessarily involve any movement of the protein but is most easily envisioned as a mechanism involving a flexible substrate and a flexible enzyme. Combination of the two to form a complex constrains and stresses both. Those substrates that bind less firmly are less strained and therefore, in general, less reactive in their complexes than are substrates bound more firmly.

The foregoing will be very difficult to distinguish experimentally from the following third possibility. It may be that the specificity contributes to the entropy of activation for the reaction by binding the substrate in such a way that its conformation in the complex is very close to that in the activated complex for the reaction. This possibility is envisioned, then, not in terms of strained bond angles or distances but in terms of restricted rotations.[3] In complexes with "good" substrates, i.e., substrates that are bound well *and* are easily reacted, the ground state is fixed in a conformation very similar to that of the transition state. For poor substrates, this is not the case, rotation about the critical bond being much freer and the correct conformation occurring only occasionally at random (22). In general, such a possibility for catalysis would be expected to be complicated by the occurrence of nonproductive complexes (including the "misorientation" factor discussed previously), and clear-cut analysis of the basis for these entropic effects in catalysis seems certain to be difficult.

NEGATIVE CATALYSIS AND SPECIFICITY

The preceding discussion has stressed the catalytic function of enzymes in lowering one component or another of the free energies of activation of the reactions they catalyze. There is another sense in which enzymic catalysis may also be considered effective. This is easily seen if one envisions a highly reactive, but essential metabolic intermediate. The tactical problem here, so to speak, is not in getting it to react but in keeping it from reacting with the wrong thing. In this situation an enzyme can be an effective agent by *raising* the free energies of activation for other reactions, whether or not it lowers that for its specific reaction. Here it is a catalyst, too, although in the negative catalytic sense, and its functional significance as an enzyme is undeniable.

Two questions must be asked regarding these considerations: What are the circumstances under which they might be applicable, and are any actual examples known? Clearly, if an enzyme is to be effective

---

[3] It will be noted that this concept is closely related to the idea of substrate orientation mentioned above in connection with substrate juxtaposition. Jencks refers to this factor as "entropic strain."

in this essentially protective function, it must bind the intermediate very tightly; there must be little free intermediate in solution. This is of course precisely the situation with many unstable metabolic intermediates, such as the adenyl amino acids in protein synthesis, which remain enzyme-bound. Moreover, the system is carried to its logical extreme, in a sense, in two-substrate substituted enzyme mechanisms, where the reactive intermediate involves modification of a group in the enzyme itself. This is either oxidation-reduction of a prosthetic group covalently bound to the enzyme or the substitution of an enzymic group with a group from the first substrate. Such an intermediate can be a highly unstable chemical species, e.g., the Schiff base intermediate in the aldolase reaction. Yet the selection of molecules with which it can in actuality react is limited because of the differences in chemical environment between the free solution and regions of the protein surface, i.e., by the specificity of the enzyme for its second substrate.

Enzymes will in general combine both positive and negative catalytic functions. All common enzyme assays are based solely on the positive component, however. It would be very interesting to look for enzymes with purely negative functions. Especially in organized substructures, one might very well expect to find molecules that serve only to bind reactive intermediates in a way preventing their reaction with the solvent water or other extraneous reagents. Although it may be difficult to devise good assay procedures for such enzymes (which are still "protein catalysts," we note, though now negative ones) there is no reason a priori to doubt their existence.

α-CHYMOTRYPSIN

An elegant application of many of the considerations on which this chapter is based has been made by Bender and Kézdy for chymotrypsin catalysis (22). The reaction features no ionic strength and dielectric constant effects and no electrophilic catalysis, but many of the other major concepts are involved. These investigators previously had analyzed the known facts about α-chymotrypsin catalysis to postulate a concerted mechanism (Fig. 16) involving both proton donation and proton acceptance by imidazoles and nucleophilic attack by a serine hydroxyl group to form the acyl enzyme (30). A similar series of events with water as the nucleophile results in deacylation. Proceeding from clear analogies in the physical organic literature, these investigators then undertook to explain all of the orders of magnitude in the rate-limiting deacylation step for this protease. That is, they sought to

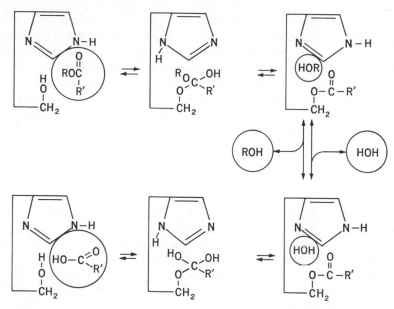

FIG. 16. The Bender-Kézdy mechanism for chymotrypsin hydrolytic action. The long line connecting the imidazole ring and the aliphatic hydroxyl group is to be understood as the protein structure that maintains these critical groups in the requisite three-dimensional array. In all diagrams, materials not bonded to the protein are circled.

account quantitatively for the entire enzymic catalysis in terms of reasonable contributing factors.

Starting with the rate constant for the hydroxide ion-catalyzed hydrolysis of N-acetyl-L-tryptophanamide (3×10^{-4} M^{-1} sec^{-1}), Bender and his co-workers converted to an imidazole general-base-catalyzed reaction (4.8×10^{-10} M^{-1} sec^{-1}), then on the basis of the 10 M approximation discussed above, to an *intra*molecular imidazole general-base-catalyzed reaction (4.8×10^{-9} sec^{-1}). The change in the nature of the rate-determining step from the hydrolysis to the alcoholysis of an amide (the attack by the serine hydroxyl) could in itself be expected to contribute a factor of about one hundredfold, so that allowance for this factor left the constant at 4.8×10^{-7} sec^{-1}. Allowance for the non-electrostatic entropy of activation (there is no electrostatic contribution), cast by these authors in terms of the freezing of substrate specificity (the last of the three possible frames of reference for this effect presented in the preceding section) introduced another factor of 10^3. This was done on the explicit assumption that the intramolecularity factor (10 M basis) did not include any component of restricted rotation. The calculated constant was thus increased to $4.8 \times 10^{-4} \text{ sec}^{-1}$. All that remained was to allow for the general-acid catalysis in the imidazole proton donation step. The chemical analogy establishing the effect of proton transfer on an ester indicates that a rate enhancement of the order of hundreds would be a proper allowance. This left a final calculated constant in the hundredths reciprocal seconds. The experimental rate constant is $4.4 \times 10^{-2} \text{ sec}^{-1}$. The agreement, proceeding from convincing chemical analogy at each step is extremely impressive.

GENERAL REFERENCES

Bender, M. L., and F. J. Kézdy: *Ann. Rev. Biochem.*, **34**: (1965).

Jencks, W. P.: *Ann. Rev. Biochem.*, **32**: (1963).

Jencks, W. P.: in N. O. Kaplan and E. P. Kennedy (eds.), *Current Aspects of Biochemical Energetics*, Academic, New York, 1966.

Koshland, D. E., Jr.: in P. D. Boyer, H. Lardy, and K. Myrbäck (eds.), *The Enzymes*, 2nd ed., Vol. 1, Academic, New York, 1959 and *Advan. Enzymol.*, **22**: (1960).

Westheimer, F. H.: *Advan. Enzymol.*, **24**: (1962).

Lumry, R.: in P. D. Boyer, H. Lardy, and K. Myrbäck (eds.), *The Enzymes*, 2nd ed., Vol. 1, Academic, New York, 1959.

Waley, S. G.: *Mechanisms of Organic and Enzymic Reactions*, Oxford, London, 1962.

SPECIFIC REFERENCES

1. Koshland, D. E., Jr.: *J. Cellular Comp. Physiol.*, **47**: Suppl. 1, 217 (1956).
2. Koshland, D. E., Jr.: *J. Theoret. Biol.*, **2**: 75 (1962).
3. Bender, M. L., Y. Chow, and F. Chloupek: *J. Am. Chem. Soc.*, **80**: 5380 (1958).
4. Bruice, T. E.: *Brookhaven Symp. Biol.*, **15**: 52 (1962).
5. Laidler, K. J.: *The Chemical Kinetics of Enzyme Action*, Oxford, London, 1958, p. 204.
6. Leininger, K., and J. Westley: *J. Biol. Chem.*, **243**: 1892 (1968).
7. Smith, E. L.: *J. Biol. Chem.*, **233**: 1392 (1958).
8. Green, J. R., and J. Westley: *J. Biol. Chem.*, **236**: 3047 (1961).
9. Westley, J., and T. Nakamoto: *J. Biol. Chem.*, **237**: 547 (1962).
10. Mintel, R.: Unpublished data.
11. Wold, F., and C. E. Ballou: *J. Biol. Chem.*, **227**: 301 (1957).
12. Williams, R. J. P.: in P. D. Boyer, H. Lardy, and K. Myrbäck (eds.), *The Enzymes*, 2nd ed., Vol. 1, Academic, New York, 1959, p. 391.
13. Vallee, B. L.: *Federation Proc.*, **23**: 8 (1964).

14. Gibbons, B. H., and J. T. Edsall: *J. Biol. Chem.*, **238**: 3502 (1963).
15. Mintel, R., and J. Westley: *J. Biol. Chem.*, **241**: 3381 (1966).
16. Metzger, H. P., and I. B. Wilson: *Biochemistry*, **3**: 926 (1964).
17. Brønsted, J. N.: *Chem. Revs.*, **5**: 231 (1928).
18. Lewis, G. N.: *J. Franklin Inst.*, **226**: 293 (1938).
19. Usanovich, M.: *J. Gen. Chem.* (*USSR*), **9**: 182 (1939).
20. Mulliken, R.: *J. Phys. Chem.*, **56**: 801 (1952).
21. Lai, C. Y., P. Hoffee, and B. L. Horecker: *Arch. Biochem. Biophys.*, **112**: 567 (1965).
22. Bender, M. L., F. J. Kézdy, and C. R. Gunter: *J. Am. Chem. Soc.*, **86**: 3714 (1964).
23. Laidler, K. J.: *The Chemical Kinetics of Enzyme Action*, Oxford, London, 1958, p. 205 ff.
24. Koshland, D. E., Jr.: *Proc. Natl. Acad. Sci. U.S.*, **44**: 98 (1958).
25. Hammes, G. G.: *Nature*, **204**: 342 (1964).
26. Reiner, J.: *Behavior of Enzyme Systems*, Burgess, Minneapolis, 1959, p. 297 ff.
27. Lumry, R.: in P. D. Boyer, H. Lardy, and K. Myrbäck (eds.), *The Enzymes*, 2nd ed., Vol. 1, Academic, New York, 1959, p. 157.
28. Jencks, W. P.: *Ann. Rev. Biochem.*, **32**: 639 (1963).
29. Jencks, W. P.: in N. O. Kaplan and E .P. Kennedy (eds.), *Current Aspects of Biochemical Energetics*, Academic, New York, 1966, p. 273.
30. Bender, M. L., and F. J. Kézdy: *J. Am. Chem. Soc.*, **86**: 3704 (1964).

PART ▌▌

THE FORMS
OF ENZYME
MECHANISMS

Much of the material in Chaps. 2, 3, and 4 applies strictly to *one-substrate reactions* only. For such reactions, the formal aspect of mechanism [i.e., the sequence of events in terms of a diagram like Eq. (6) of Chap. 2, for example] is unambiguous and easy to analyze. Unfortunately, however, nearly all enzyme-catalyzed reactions involve at least two substrates,[1] a fact which has until recently prevented unequivocal kinetic analysis of enzyme mechanisms. Nevertheless, Koshland's suggestion of the single and double displacement basis for classifying transferase reactions, analogous to the SN_1 and SN_2 classification of organic mechanisms, did make possible a fruitful consideration of the formal aspect of a number of two-substrate mechanisms. Even more important, this proposal more than any other was instrumental in dispelling the aura of mysticism that had invested much thought on the action of enzymes. Even those of us badly contaminated by the supernaturalism surrounding the arts of enzyme isolation were thus fortified with the will to regard enzymes precisely as chemical entities, confident that this view could ultimately provide a complete basis for understanding their catalytic properties. The subsequent developments of clear-cut steady-state kinetic analysis of two-substrate reactions and the continuing development of the pre-steady-state kinetic methods have now permitted relatively easy demonstration of the formal mechanisms of many enzyme-catalyzed reactions.

[1] This is not always immediately evident, as when one of the substrates is the solvent water.

7

SINGLE- AND DOUBLE-DISPLACEMENT
MECHANISMS

Until the 1950s most work that had explicitly taken two substrates into account had presumed that an essential part of any enzyme mechanism must be an intermediate ternary complex involving the enzyme and both substrates. An outstanding exception, however, was the work of Doudoroff, Barker, and Hassid (1), who had presented evidence strongly suggesting that the mechanism of the sucrose phosphorylase reaction involves the intermediate formation of a glucosyl enzyme:[1]

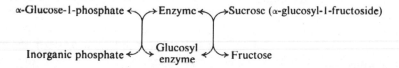

In the absence of fructose or other glucosyl acceptor, this highly specific enzyme catalyzed a rapid exchange reaction between glucose-1-phosphate and radioactive inorganic phosphate or between the sugar phosphate and arsenate. Since glycosyl arsenates hydrolyze spontaneously, the overall reaction in the presence of arsenate was the enzyme-catalyzed hydrolysis of glucose-1-phosphate.

The methods used in inferring this formal mechanism were expanded and generalized by Koshland (4) to provide a basis for making the distinction between what he termed single- and double-displacement mechanisms. This is essentially the distinction between mechanisms involving ternary complexes of enzyme with both intact substrates and

---

[1] The inferred existence of this form recently was confirmed both by kinetic analysis (2) and by isolation (3).

those like that of sucrose phosphorylase, which involve an intermediate substituted enzyme. In the former type of mechanism, the single displacements, the substrates are bound at spatially adjacent positions on the enzyme,[2] which facilitates a direct interaction between them (Fig. 17). One reaction occurs, a single displacement. In contrast, the double-displacement or substituted enzyme mechanism involves reaction of the enzyme first with one substrate to form the substituted enzyme and one final product. The substituted enzyme then takes part in a second displacement reaction with the other substrate, to regenerate the free enzyme and form the second final product.

The criteria for distinguishing between single- and double-displacement mechanisms experimentally have been much discussed. As originally stated by Koshland, they involved principally the isotope exchange and specificity criteria used for sucrose phosphorylase, with the addition of the question of inversion or retention of optical configuration, in cases where an asymmetric center is at the reaction site in the substrate. Thus for sucrose phosphorylase itself it is important to note that both the glucose-1-phosphate and the sucrose taking part in the reaction are of the α configuration. Presumably the glucosyl enzyme is β. The reasoning follows the usual rule (inversion results from an odd number of displacements, retention from an even number) and gives a result in agreement with the other data for this enzyme.

A considerable number of enzymes have been shown to display the behavior expected for double-displacement mechanisms, including good catalysis of an appropriate exchange reaction and retention of optical configuration in the product. On the other hand, numerous transfer reactions have failed to display such behavior, showing inversion of configuration in the product and no exchange in the absence of both substrates. For example, the maltose phosphorylase reaction (6) provides a strong contrast with the sucrose phosphorylase reaction. There is no exchange of phosphate with either α- or β-glucose-1-phosphate in the absence of an acceptor sugar, and phosphorolysis of maltose (α-glucosyl glucoside) yields β-glucose-1-phosphate, a net inversion of configuration. A single-displacement mechanism was inferred from these observations (6).

---

[2] Alternatively, a binary complex may be formed between the enzyme and one substrate, which is then attacked by the second substrate, with formation of no ternary complex having a lifetime longer than the activated complex of transition state theory, or at any rate no complex having a lifetime so long that its decomposition can be made to limit the overall reaction velocity. This is the Theorell–Chance mechanism (5); it too involves only a single displacement reaction.

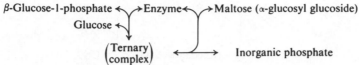

In general, such observations have been taken as reasonable permissive evidence for tentative assignment of single- or double-displacement mechanisms. Since any information relating to the form of a catalytic mechanism is invaluable in guiding further work, the result has been a prolonged burst of interest and investigation in enzymic mechanisms.

There has been some much-deserved criticism of the indiscriminate use of the isotope exchange criterion (7,8). Exchange of a portion of the substrate is evidence for a double displacement only under certain circumstances. In terms of the exchange of inorganic phosphate into glucose-1-phosphate in the sucrose phosphorylase case discussed above, it would be necessary to show also that there is a binding site for fructose and that phosphate is unlikely to be able to occupy it. Otherwise, a single-displacement type mechanism could yield exchange, with phosphate as the acceptor substrate; the first substrate and the product would both be glucose-1-phosphate. In the present case, the conclusion of the double-displacement form is made more likely by both the specificity requirements for fructose and by the retention of configuration, a result that could occur in a single displacement only by so-called frontside attack, which is judged unlikely. Nevertheless, where exchange occurs, it is clear that assignments on the basis of the criteria given above always involve matters of judgment regarding the adequacy of the specificity requirements and the unlikelihood of frontside attack.

A study illustrating proper caution in the interpretation of exchange data is that of Sörbo (9), who found that sulfite (SO_3^{2-}) could serve as an acceptor substrate for the transferable sulfur atom from thiosulfate (SSO_3^{2-}) in the reaction catalyzed by rhodanese. This observation might have been interpreted as indicating a double-displacement mechanism, formally just like the sucrose phosphorylase mechanism.

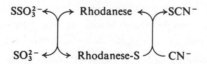

Instead, however, Sörbo concluded simply that sulfite is an alternate acceptor substrate for the enzyme, taking over the role of cyanide, without implications for the formal mechanism. In this view, the observation fits a Theorell–Chance mechanism

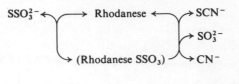

or

$$SSO_3^{2-} \leftarrow \quad\longleftarrow \text{Rhodanese} \quad \leftarrow \quad\longrightarrow \overset{*}{S}SO_3^{2-}$$
$$\longrightarrow SO_3^{2-}$$
$$\longrightarrow (\text{Rhodanese SSO}_3) \longrightarrow \overset{*}{S}O_3^{2-}$$

or other single-displacement mechanism as well as it does the double displacement. Without additional information, no formal mechanistic conclusion would have been appropriate, even though the specificity of rhodanese for cyanide had been thought absolute up to that time, as sulfite and cyanide are both excellent sulfur nucleophiles.

The point of the above account is that, especially in the absence of any possibility of applying configuration criteria, the finding of exchange (even with high specificity for acceptor substrate) cannot lead unambiguously to a conclusion regarding the formal mechanism. The subsequent finding that the rhodanese mechanism is in fact a double displacement required further experimental work.

Moreover, even where configuration data are applicable, it appears that the assumption of the unlikelihood of frontside attack may be a poor one. The X-ray crystallographic structures of the lysozyme-substrate complex, for example, suggest that frontside attack may occur in this highly constrained situation (10). There is, in any case, no a priori reason to believe that frontside attack might not occur in the active site cleft of an enzyme, even if it is an unusual occurrence in free solution.

Besides these uncertainties in interpreting a positive result in exchange experiments, there is also a problem in interpreting a negative result. In fact, where no exchange occurs, no conclusion whatever may be drawn from this single observation, as the position of equilibrium in the first reaction of a double displacement might preclude the observation of exchange.[3] In some such cases, however, study of the exchange reactions for both forward and reverse directions can lead to

[3] Although in principle, exchange should be observed unless the first reaction is entirely irreversible, the practical matters of obtainable specific radioactivities, etc., do place limitations on the experimental observations.

a definite conclusion. For example, Koshland (11) found that no exchange occurred between isotopically labeled adenosine and adenylic acid in the presence of 3'-nucleotidase. Similarly, the enzyme failed to catalyze isotope exchange between inorganic phosphate and water. Considered in terms of a possible double-displacement mechanism, these results could be interpreted unequivocally.

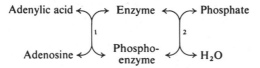

The particular circumstances of the first experiment made it possible to calculate that $k_{-1} < k_{+2}$. Similarly, the limit placed by the second experiment was $k_{-2} < 10^{-3}k_{+1}$. Thus, to be consistent with these results, the hydrolysis rate for the enzyme under these conditions and the double-displacement formal mechanism, the overall equilibrium constant would have to be large:

$$K_{eq} = \frac{k_{+2}k_{+1}}{k_{-1}k_{-2}} > 10^3$$

In fact, however, the overall equilibrium constant is near unity and the double-displacement mechanism must therefore be incorrect. In this way the negative results of exchange experiments can sometimes be used to eliminate the double-displacement possibility conclusively.

Perhaps the most convincing single piece of evidence for a double-displacement mechanism is the isolation of the substituted enzyme from reaction mixtures under conditions suitable for the overall reaction except for the absence of the second substrate. If this can be achieved and the isolated protein shown to contain the substrate group to be transferred but not the remainder of the group donor substrate, the case is very strong. If, furthermore, the isolated intermediate can be shown to react rapidly with the appropriate second substrate to yield the second product and, perhaps, with the first product to reform the first substrate, the proof is complete. The approach is so straightforward that it does not require to be dwelt on here. The method is not of general applicability, however, there being no substitute for luck in finding a substituted enzyme intermediate sufficiently stable to permit isolation. There are, nevertheless, a few such cases in the literature, among which the acyl-α-chymotrypsin (12), the sulfur-substituted rhodanese (13,14) and the coenzyme A transferase-CoA intermediate (15,16), for example, appear to meet all the criteria simply.

GENERAL REFERENCES

Koshland, D. E. Jr.: in W. McElroy and B. Glass (eds.), *Mechanisms of Enzyme Action*, The Johns Hopkins Press, Baltimore, 1954.

SPECIFIC REFERENCES

1. Doudoroff, M., H. A. Barker, and W. Z. Hassid: *J. Biol. Chem.*, **168**: 725 (1947).
2. Silverstein, R., J. Voet, D. Reed, and R. H. Abeles: *J. Biol. Chem.*, **242**: 1338 (1967).
3. Voet, J., and R. H. Abeles: *Federation Proc.*, **26**: 389 (1967).
4. Koshland, D. E., Jr.: in W. McElroy and B. Glass (eds.), *Mechanisms of Enzyme Action*, The Johns Hopkins Press, Baltimore, 1954, p. 608.
5. Theorell, H., and B. Chance: *Acta Chem. Scand.*, **5**: 1127 (1951).
6. Fitting, C., and M. Doudoroff: *J. Biol. Chem.*, **199**: 153 (1952).
7. Boyer, P. D.: *Ann. Rev. Biochem.*, **29**: 15 (1960).
8. Jencks, W. P.: *Ann. Rev. Biochem.*, **32**: 639 (1963).
9. Sörbo, B. H.: *Acta Chem. Scand.*, **11**: 628 (1957).
10. Blake, C. C. F., L. N. Johnson, G. A. Mair, A. C. T. North, D. C. Phillips, and V. R. Sarma: *Proc. Roy. Soc.* (*London*), *Ser. B*, **167**: 385 (1967).
11. Koshland, D. E., Jr.: *Discussions Faraday Soc.*, **20**: 142 (1955).
12. Kézdy, F. J., G. E. Clement, and M. L. Bender: *J. Am. Chem. Soc.*, **86**: 3690 (1964).
13. Green, J., and J. Westley: *J. Biol. Chem.*, **236**: 3047 (1961).
14. Westley, J., and T. Nakamoto: *J. Biol. Chem.*, **237**: 547 (1962).
15. Hersh, L. B., and W. P. Jencks: *J. Biol. Chem.*, **242**: 3468 (1967).
16. Hersh, L. B., and W. P. Jencks: *J. Biol. Chem.*, **242**: 3481 (1967).

8

SUBSTITUTED ENZYMES
AND TERNARY COMPLEXES

In nearly all of the early discussions regarding the criteria for assignment of the formal aspect of mechanisms, the kinetic approach was ignored. It is usually possible, however, to determine unambiguously by kinetic means whether a two-substrate mechanism involves a ternary complex of enzyme with both intact substrates or, alternatively, a substituted enzyme.[1] Pertinent developments of steady-state kinetic theory have been provided by Alberty (1,2), Dalziel (3,4), Frieden (5), Cleland (6), and Wong and Hanes (7). By exhaustive consideration of a kinetic scheme sufficiently complex to encompass all of the possible permutations and combinations of two-substrate mechanisms, the latter authors have firmly established an unequivocal basis for the experimental kinetic analysis of such systems. For example, they have shown that Dalziel's kinetic distinction of substituted enzyme mechanisms from other mechanisms is both general and exclusive. In a parallel development, Cleland has done a great deal to implement the application of such distinctions in experimental work.

The mathematical techniques that have made exhaustive consideration of mechanisms feasible were derived by King and Altman (8) and somewhat modified by Volkenstein and Goldstein (9). These methods involve diagrammatic procedures based on the use of determinants for solving the simultaneous equations that describe a mechanism. Although the King and Altman method is clearly the procedure of choice for deriving rate equations for new mechanisms, it will not be detailed here[2]

---

[1] To establish the proper perspective for further reading in this field, note that the double displacement intermediate consisting of the enzyme bearing the transferable group from the first substrate is variously referred to as a substituted enzyme, an enzyme-substrate compound (*not* "complex") and a covalent enzyme-substrate intermediate.

[2] An account of this method in usable form may be found in the first general reference cited at the end of the chapter.

for two reasons: (a) Extensive compilations of rate equations for all common mechanisms are available in the literature (1–7) and Cleland's excellent recent review (10) tabulates and compares the different nomenclatures used by most of these authors. (b) It seems more important to stress the *understanding* of the equations to be gained through analogy to and continuity with the treatment of one-substrate kinetics presented in Part I of this book.

SUBSTITUTED ENZYME MECHANISMS

The kinetic analysis of two-substrate mechanisms involving substituted enzyme intermediates (Fig. 17) yields two characteristic features: all such mechanisms must give straight lines in the linear plotting forms[3]; moreover, the kinetic plots for A at different constant concentrations of B all display the same value of K_m^{app}/V^{app}. Thus substituted enzyme mechanisms are formally analogous to the relief of uncompetitive inhibition; i.e., the double reciprocal plots are a set of parallel straight lines (Fig. 17).

The key to understanding this form lies in taking notice of the discharge of the first product from the enzyme before the second substrate must attach; i.e., in attending the double-displacement character of the reaction. It is this feature that isolates the reactions of the first and second substrates, rendering both essentially irreversible at initial rates in the absence of products. The important feature is the initial irreversibility of reactions that discharge products into solution at zero concentration.

The second substrate, then, has no direct effect on any reaction involving the first, as it is simply not present on the enzyme until after the first substrate has been split. The sole effect of the second substrate on the kinetic behavior of the first results from its regeneration of free enzyme. Thus a higher concentration of second substrate means only a higher proportion of E_0 in the free enzyme form. This is formally analogous to the relief of uncompetitive inhibition in a one-substrate system, where the inhibitor acts solely to *prevent* regeneration of free enzyme from an enzymic intermediate.

The correctness of this formal analogy is seen in the form of the kinetic curves for the substituted enzyme. Steady-state derivation (see

---

[3] Substrate inhibition, which again introduces two enzymic forms for combination with a substrate, can modify this consideration, as it does for one-substrate mechanisms.

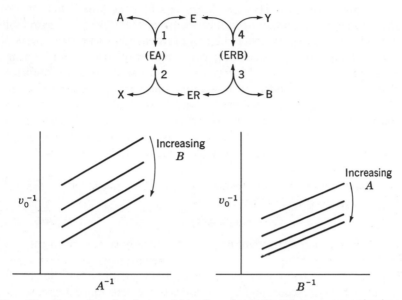

FIG. 17. Formal mechanism and kinetics of substituted enzyme mechanism (also known as double-displacement, transaminase-type, or ping-pong mechanism). Either of the unstable intermediates (enclosed in parentheses) may be kinetically insignificant.

below) of the initial velocity equation in reciprocal form yields

$$v_0^{-1} = E_0^{-1}\left(\frac{k_{+2} + k_{+4}}{k_{+2}k_{+4}}\right)\left(\frac{K_m^A}{A} + \frac{K_m^B}{B} + 1\right) \tag{34}$$

For reciprocal plots where A is the substrate varied, the slope contains no term in B. Similarly, the slope of plots of v_0^{-1} vs. $[B]^{-1}$ does not vary with $[A]$. Parallel reciprocal plots for either substrate are obtained for different concentrations of the other substrate. That this behavior is characteristic of substituted enzyme mechanisms has been widely recognized; that in principle it may be used to eliminate all other reasonable mechanistic forms follows again from the exhaustive nature of modern theoretical treatments. It has also been shown that inclusion of "dead-end" complex formation (i.e., the formation of nonproductive complexes of B with E and of A with ER) in substituted enzyme mechanisms does not make the identification of this form equivocal (11). In fact the occurrence of this characteristic double competitive substrate inhibition can greatly facilitate the steady-state diagnosis of the substituted enzyme form (12).

From these considerations, it appears that the kinetic behavior of the substituted enzyme or double-displacement form is reasonable both on an intuitive level and in terms of its characteristic rate equation. We shall hope to deal successfully with single-displacement mechanisms on a similar basis. First, however, it may be well to assure ourselves that Eq. (34) does indeed follow from the formal mechanism given. For this one case, then (not that we seriously doubt the correctness of the equation but for the opportunity to improve our understanding of it), we shall derive the rate equation, using exactly the same simple procedures used earlier in deriving rate equations for the one-substrate reaction schemes.

Referring to the double-displacement form presented in Fig. 17, we can express initial velocity as

$$v_0 = k_{+4}(ERB) = k_{+2}(EA) \tag{35}$$

All of the enzymic forms will be present at steady-state concentration if we use a suitably high ratio of initial concentrations of substrates to enzyme. Concentrations of both the products X and Y will be zero at initial velocity. Accordingly, we can write equations describing the initial steady-state concentration of each enzymic form.

$$\frac{d(EA)}{dt} = k_{+1}AE - k_{-1}(EA) - k_{+2}(EA) = 0$$

$$\therefore \quad (EA) = \frac{k_{+1}AE}{k_{-1} + k_{+2}} \tag{36}$$

$$\frac{d(ER)}{dt} = k_{+2}(EA) - k_{+3}B(ER) + k_{-3}(ERB) = 0$$

$$\therefore \quad (ER) = \frac{k_{+2}(EA) + k_{-3}(ERB)}{k_{+3}B} \tag{37}$$

$$\frac{d(ERB)}{dt} = k_{+3}B(ER) - k_{-3}(ERB) - k_{+4}(ERB) = 0$$

Substituting from Eqs. (36) and (37),

$$(ERB) = \frac{k_{+3}B(ER)}{k_{-3} + k_{+4}} = \frac{k_{+3}B\left[\dfrac{[(k_{+2}k_{+1}AE)/(k_{-1} + k_{+2})] + k_{-3}(ERB)}{k_{+3}B}\right]}{k_{-3} + k_{+4}}$$

from which,

$$(ERB) = \frac{k_{+2}k_{+1}AE}{k_{+4}(k_{-1} + k_{+2})} \tag{38}$$

Combining with Eq. (35),

$$v_0 = k_{+4}\left[\frac{k_{+2}k_{+1}AE}{k_{+4}(k_{-1} + k_{+2})}\right] \tag{39}$$

Equation (39) is pleasingly simple, but it suffers from the disadvantage that the enzyme concentration term represents only the free form rather than total enzyme. We need an enzyme conservation equation:

$$E_0 = E + (EA) + (ER) + (ERB) \qquad (40)$$

where (EA) is given by Eq. (36), (ER) by Eq. (37), and (ERB) by Eq. 38. This equation sorts out to

$$E = \frac{E_0}{1 + \dfrac{k_{+1}A}{k_{-1} + k_{+2}} + \dfrac{k_{+1}k_{+2}A}{k_{+3}B(k_{-1} + k_{+2})} + \dfrac{k_{+1}k_{+2}k_{-3}A}{k_{+3}k_{+4}B(k_{-1} + k_{+2})} + \dfrac{k_{+1}k_{+2}A}{k_{+4}(k_{-1} + k_{+2})}}$$

$$(41)$$

When we multiply both numerator and denominator of Eq. (41) by $k_{+3}k_{+4}B(k_{-1} + k_{+2})$ and substitute it into Eq. (39), we obtain

$$v_0 = \frac{k_{+1}k_{+2}k_{+3}k_{+4}ABE_0}{k_{+3}k_{+4}B(k_{-1} + k_{+2}) + k_{+1}k_{+3}k_{+4}AB + k_{+1}k_{+2}A(k_{-3} + k_{+4}) + k_{+1}k_{+2}k_{+3}AB} \qquad (42)$$

A reciprocal form of Eq. (42) is

$$v_0^{-1} = E_0^{-1}\left(\frac{k_{-1} + k_{+2}}{k_{+1}k_{+2}A} + \frac{k_{-3} + k_{+4}}{k_{+3}k_{+4}B} + \frac{k_{+2} + k_{+4}}{k_{+2}k_{+4}}\right) \qquad (43)$$

or, converting to the form of Eq. (34),

$$v_0^{-1} = E_0^{-1}\left(\frac{k_{+2} + k_{+4}}{k_{+2}k_{+4}}\right)\left(\frac{K_m^A}{A} + \frac{K_m^B}{B} + 1\right)$$

where

$$K_m^A = \frac{k_{+4}(k_{-1} + k_{+2})}{k_{+1}(k_{+2} + k_{+4})}$$

and

$$K_m^B = \frac{k_{+2}(k_{-3} + k_{+4})}{k_{+3}(k_{+2} + k_{+4})}$$

These definitions of K_m are more complex than those in the one-substrate case dealt with earlier but they have the analogous functional meaning; e.g., K_m^A is the concentration of A yielding half the maximal velocity in the presence of saturating concentrations of B. It should also be noted that the maximum velocity of this system is

$$V = E_0\left(\frac{k_{+2}k_{+4}}{k_{+2} + k_{+4}}\right)$$

What the foregoing derivation demonstrates, beyond the fact that Eq. (34) is legitimate, is that rate equations for two-substrate mechanisms can be obtained by exactly the same procedures as those used for one-substrate mechanisms. The manipulations are just much more cumbersome.

TERNARY COMPLEX MECHANISMS

As with the substituted enzyme mechanisms, all mechanisms involving the obligatory formation of a ternary complex can also be formulated analogously to the modifier mechanisms dealt with in a previous chapter. Consider the case where Q, the modifier, now becomes B, the second substrate. Figure 18(a) shows the essential alteration for one style of mechanism (obligate sequence of attachment) in which the formation of product and regeneration of free enzyme result from the breakdown of a ternary complex of enzyme with both substrates. Thus the rate constant for the breakdown of (EA) to product and free enzyme in the one-substrate formulation is zero and other unimolecular steps govern the maximum velocity. The formal analogy to the situation showing noncompetitive inhibition in the one-substrate mechanism is rather obvious, the only difference being that in this case reaction of (EA) with B promotes rather than inhibits the formation of products. Moreover, this case contrasts with the substituted enzyme mechanism in that reactions 1 and 2 are here not isolated from each other by the discharge of a product. Thus both (EA) and E are affected by the presence of B. The steady-state rate equation for this formal mechanism is

$$v_0^{-1} = E_0^{-1}\left(\frac{k_{+3}+k_{+4}}{k_{+3}k_{+4}}\right)\left[\frac{K_m^A}{A} + \frac{K_m^B}{B} + 1 + \frac{k_{-1}k_{+4}(k_{-2}+k_{+3})}{k_{+1}k_{+2}(k_{+3}+k_{+4})AB}\right] \qquad (44)$$

The most obvious difference between Eqs. (44) and (34), which describes the substituted enzyme form, is the occurrence here of the last term. This term, which involves concentrations of both A and B and is not present in Eq. (34), ensures that both the slopes and intercepts of plots of v_0^{-1} against A^{-1} will vary with B and those of v_0^{-1} against B^{-1} will vary with A. Characteristic initial velocity patterns are shown in Fig. 18(a). With the exception of this last term, however, the two equations are very similar. The term

$$E_0\left(\frac{k_{+3}k_{+4}}{k_{+3}+k_{+4}}\right)$$

in Eq. (44) is the maximum velocity of this obligate sequence or ordered ternary complex form. Also as in the substituted enzyme form, the K_m values are the respective substrate concentrations yielding half maximum velocity each in the presence of saturating concentrations of the other substrate.

$$K_m^A = \frac{k_{+3}k_{+4}}{k_{+1}(k_{+3}+k_{+4})} \qquad \text{and} \qquad K_m^B = \frac{k_{+4}(k_{-2}+k_{+3})}{k_{+2}(k_{+3}+k_{+4})}$$

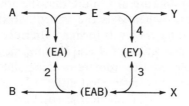

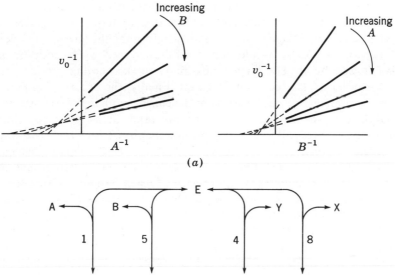

FIG. 18. (a) Form and kinetics of ternary complex mechanism (also known as single-displacement, dehydrogenase type or sequential mechanism) of the obligate sequence or ordered type. Not all of the unstable intermediates (enclosed in parentheses) need be kinetically significant. (b) Form of general ternary complex mechanism, encompassing random sequence mechanisms and including the possibility of isomerization of the ternary complex.

It is interesting and useful to note that the double reciprocal lines obtained in this form when A is the varied substrate and B is held constant at several different levels form a pattern converging in a point that represents an interaction of A and the enzyme on which B has no effect. In fact the abscissal coordinate of this point is $-1/K_s^A$ or $-K_1$. The second substrate does in general affect K_m^A but certainly not K_s^A.[4] Clearly, use of this fact to evaluate the equilibrium constant requires that one know which is the first substrate, i.e., which adds to the free enzyme (see below).

The category of ternary complex mechanisms also includes more complicated forms, which can be discussed in terms of Fig. 18(b). What is indicated there is the possibility of forming the ternary complex in two different ways, by addition of A followed by B *and* by addition of B followed by A. The further possibility of discharging products in either order is also taken into account. Finally, the occurrence of two ternary complexes, one consisting of the enzyme with the two substrates and the other of the enzyme with the two products, is indicated. This, then, is a very general ternary complex mechanism, which reduces to the "ordered" form discussed above when the overall velocity through steps 1–4 greatly exceeds that through steps 5–8 and the interconversion of the ternary complexes is rapid relative to step 3 or step 4, or both.

In general, the random-order mechanism shown in Fig. 18(b) does not display kinetic behavior of the normal hyperbolic form; the normal linear plotting forms do not yield straight lines. All linear (unbranched) formal mechanisms give rise to straight-line plots in the usual plotting forms, a consequence of the involvement of substrate concentration terms to the first power only, and are said to be first degree in substrate. However, mechanisms with branch points, which thus provide more than one enzymic form with which a substrate can react on the way to products, are in general second or higher degree in that substrate. For this reason such mechanisms may yield curved plots. On the other hand, there are several circumstances under which the plots will *not* be discernibly curved. One of these is the occurrence of rapid equilibrium among all enzymic forms except the two ternary complexes.

The rapid-equilibrium random mechanism yields straight double reciprocal plots converging to the left of the ordinate axis. These initial velocity patterns are indistinguishable from those of the ordered ternary complex mechanism, reflecting a rate equation of the same form. These two formal mechanisms can, however, be distinguished by product inhibition studies (see below).

---

[4] Again, be reminded that however K_m^A is defined in terms of a particular collection of rate constants, K_s^A is simply the dissociation constant of the complex of free enzyme with A.

When, in addition to the occurrence of equilibrium, the attachment of each substrate to the enzyme is *completely* independent of the other, the point of convergence of the double reciprocal plots is on the abscissa. Convergence above the abscissa indicates that attachment of the constant substrate facilitates attachment of the varied substrate; convergence below the abscissa indicates that attachment of the one hinders attachment of the other. Complete independence of attachment thus simplifies the general rate equation for the rapid equilibrium formal mechanism:

$$\frac{V}{v_0} = \left(\frac{K_m^A}{A} + 1\right)\left(\frac{K_m^B}{B} + 1\right) \quad \text{or} \quad v_0 = \frac{AV/(BK_2 + 1)}{K_1^{-1} + A}$$

In the second of these forms, we recognize this equation as identical to Eq. (21) of Chap. 4, which was obtained as a description of pure noncompetitive behavior in a one-substrate equilibrium involving an inhibitor or activator. Here again, as in the pattern of plots, we see the formal analogy between noncompetitive behavior and ternary-complex formal mechanisms.

There are other conditions under which random mechanisms may yield straight linear plots. Cleland has noted that there are circumstances in which the higher order terms in substrate concentration cancel exactly. Moreover, since such terms occur in both the numerators and denominators of the rate equations, they often nearly cancel, so that unrealistic demands would be placed on the kinetic data for the curvature to be discernible. The situation relates in part to that discussed by Reiner for the curvature that should be seen in plots of data obtained in a one-substrate system with a mixture of enzymes acting on the same substrate (13). There the conclusion was that the K_m values of two enzymes might have to differ by a factor of two for any curvature to be seen.

The term "ternary complex mechanisms" should not be taken to mean that all mechanisms yielding converging plots must have *kinetically significant* ternary complexes. Consider the ordered mechanism shown in Fig. 18(a). Suppose that step 3 is very rapid and step 4 very slow (the "Theorell–Chance mechanism"). The results will be that step 4 will dominate the maximum velocity and the concentration of the ternary complex will be very low, even at maximum velocity. In short, the occurrence of the ternary complex will not be kinetically significant in the usual sense. The initial velocity patterns will, however, be of the converging kind characteristic of the ternary complex mechanisms. The rate equation is of the same form as Eq. (44), only the composition of the kinetic coefficients is different:

$$v_0^{-1} = E_0^{-1}\left(\frac{1}{k_{+4}}\right)\left(\frac{K_m^A}{A} + \frac{K_m^B}{B} + 1 + \frac{k_{-1}k_{+4}}{k_{+1}k_{+2}AB}\right)$$

The Michaelis constants retain their same operational meaning but now $K_m^A = k_{+4}/k_{+1}$ and $K_m^B = k_{+4}/k_{+2}$, while $V = k_{+4} E_0$. Some means available for distinguishing this variant of the ternary complex mechanisms are dealt with in Chaps. 9 and 10.

It is also entirely possible (and rather likely) that in any of these mechanisms a multiplicity of ternary complexes occurs. This may be a variety of complexes either in parallel, along the lines of the discussion of "misorientation" in an earlier chapter, or in series, with sequential transformation of the substrates to products, involving a number of chemically distinct ternary complexes. For the latter case, Bloomfield et al. (2) have shown that the form of the rate equation is independent of the number of intermediates and the rate constants evaluated assuming the minimum number of intermediates are minimum estimates of the true rate constants. The same is true of the substituted enzyme mechanisms.

There has been some careful consideration of circumstances in which ternary complex mechanisms might yield apparently parallel reciprocal plots like the substituted enzyme mechanisms (14,15). This would be the case, for example, if complex formation with the first substrate in a ternary complex mechanism were essentially irreversible for reasons other than the discharge of a product at zero concentration as in the substituted enzyme mechanism. It is a bit difficult to envision the circumstances in which this could be a difficulty in principle, but it is clear that there can be practical situations in which the initial velocity data available make the determination of formal mechanism difficult. Probably most such cases can be dealt with by use of either of the plotting forms (v_0 against v_0/A or A/v_0 against A) in which the ratio of apparent K_m and V values occurs as an intercept rather than as a slope. Alternatively, Slater (16) has suggested plotting K_m^{app} against V^{app}, which should be a linear function passing through the origin for substituted enzyme mechanisms (i.e., the apparent kinetic coefficients are strictly proportional). The use of statistical methods (17) for evaluating the apparent coefficients in this connection should minimize the difficulty. Koster and Veeger (14) have also found that inclusion of constant levels of a competitive inhibitor for the constant substrate may aid in the analysis.

Some parts of the foregoing discussion suggest that valuable kinetic information might be lost if no means were available for distinguishing which substrate attaches first. Two means to this end have been suggested: the systematic use of product inhibition and the use of mixed alternate substrates. The former idea is illustrated in Figs. 17 and 18, which show that only the first substrate and the last product should show mutually

TABLE 3. *Kinetic Character of Product Inhibition with One Varied Substrate and Other Substrates at Saturation*

There are three significant questions:

1. *Is* there inhibition under these conditions? i.e., Is v_0 diminished in a way that is not overcome by maintaining saturation in the nonvaried substrate(s)?

2. *If so*, is *V* altered? i.e., Is v_0 diminished even at saturation in the varied substrate? *If not*, inhibition is competitive.

3. *If so*, is K_m also altered in the same proportion? i.e., Is there isolation[a] of the inhibitor reaction from that of the varied substrate? *If so*, the inhibition is uncompetitive; *if not*, noncompetitive.

[a] Kinetic isolation is the result of an intervening reaction involving either discharge of a product at zero concentration or entry of a substrate present at saturation. This is isolation in the same sense that two halves of a double-displacement mechanism are isolated by discharge of the first product.

competitive behavior in either substituted enzyme or obligate sequence ternary complex mechanisms. Furthermore, only in substituted enzyme mechanisms in which the substrates interact in a single active site region should the first product be competitive with either substrate, in this case, the second substrate. Reasoning of this kind makes initial velocity studies in the presence of single products a very valuable technique.[5] Table 3 indicates the decisions to be made in designing such experiments and interpreting the results. Cleland (6) has laid heavy emphasis on this kind of work. The second of the Cleland papers in this series deals in detail with product inhibition; the third, which deals with the prediction of initial velocity patterns by inspection, is particularly recommended for study.

A second technique, suggested by Wong and Hanes (7) involves the use of alternate substrates. Consider what happens when, in an obligate sequence mechanism for substrates *A* and *B*, a mixture of two *A* substrates is used, call them A_1 and A_2. If *A* is the first substrate on the enzyme, *B* will now have two enzymic forms (A_1E) and (A_2E) with which to react. The result will be a mechanism now second degree in *B* and the standard plots will be curved unless A_1 and A_2 coincidentally have identical effects of K_m^B. If, however, *A* is the *second* substrate, *B* reacts only with free *E* and no increase in degree results. This behavior permits the experimental distinction of first and second substrates.

[5] This technique is valuable, too, in verifying the inferences made from initial velocity patterns and for distinguishing among the various ternary complex mechanisms. Some examples are given in the following chapters.

The method has no application to substituted enzyme mechanisms as both substrates are not present on the enzyme simultaneously. It should be noted that this test for distinguishing which is the first substrate in an obligate sequence ternary complex mechanism may not suffer from the disadvantage of difficulty in seeing the curvature mentioned above. Here the possibilities of manipulating the ratio of mixed substrates and for direct comparison of data from mixed substrate and single substrate experiments in the same system favors obtaining discernible curvature in the appropriate situation.

Finally, use may be made of the so-called "Haldane relationships" in distinguishing among different ternary complex mechanisms. In any reversible enzyme-catalyzed reaction, the overall equilibrium constant is not simply equal to the ratio of maximum velocities for the two directions but involves the K_m terms as well. For the simple one-substrate case, the Haldane relationship is

$$K_{eq} = \frac{(K_{m-})V_+}{(K_{m+})V_-}$$

where $+$ and $-$ designate the constants for the forward and reverse directions, respectively. More complex Haldane relationships are obtained for two-substrate mechanisms, some of which are useful in deciding among possible forms. Alberty (1,2), Dalziel (3), Wong and Hanes (7), and Cleland (6) have compiled listings of Haldane relationships derived for various two-substrate mechanisms.

GENERAL REFERENCES

Mahler, H. R., and E. H. Cordes: *Biological Chemistry*, Harper & Row, New York, 1966.

Dixon, M., and E. C. Webb: *Enzymes*, 2nd ed., Academic, New York, 1964.

Fisher, J. R., and V. D. Hoagland, Jr.: *A Systematic Approach to Kinetic Studies of Enzyme Systems*, Bulletin No. 26, Division of Biology and Medicine, U.S. Atomic Energy Commission.

SPECIFIC REFERENCES

1. Alberty, R. A.: *Advan. Enzymol.*, **17**: 1 (1956).
2. Bloomfield, V., L. Peller, and R. A. Alberty: *J. Am. Chem. Soc.*, **84**: 4367 (1962).
3. Dalziel, K.: *Acta Chem. Scand.*, **11**: 1706 (1957).
4. Dalziel, K.: *Trans. Faraday Soc.*, **54**: 1247 (1958).
5. Frieden, C.: *J. Am. Chem. Soc.*, **79**: 1894 (1957).

6. Cleland, W. W.: *Biochim. Biophys. Acta*, **67**: 104, 173, 188 (1963).
7. Wong, J. T., and C. S. Hanes: *Canad. J. Biochem. Physiol.*, **40**: 763 (1962).
8. King, E. L., and C. Altman: *J. Phys. Chem.*, **60**: 1375 (1956).
9. Volkenstein, M. V., and B. N. Goldstein: *Biochim. Biophys. Acta*, **115**: 471 (1966).
10. Cleland, W. W.: *Ann. Rev. Biochem.*, **36**: 77 (1967).
11. Volini, M., and J. Westley: *J. Biol. Chem.*, **241**: 5168 (1966).
12. Grisolia, S., and W. W. Cleland: *Biochemistry*, **7**: 1115 (1968).
13. Reiner, J. M.: *Behavior of Enzyme Systems*, Burgess, Minneapolis, 1959, pp. 99–102.
14. Koster, J. F., and C. Veeger: *Biochim. Biophys. Acta*, **151**: 11 (1968).
15. Copley, M., and H. T. Fromm: *Biochemistry*, **6**: 3503 (1967).
16. Slater, E. C.: *Discussions Faraday Soc.*, **20**: 231 (1955).
17. Cleland, W. W.: *Advan. Enzymol.*, **29**: 1 (1967).

9

STEADY-STATE KINETIC ANALYSIS
OF TWO-SUBSTRATE
FORMAL MECHANISMS

The previous chapter carried the implication that the fundamental forms of enzyme mechanisms can often be determined unambiguously by rather simple kinetic means. One determines the initial reaction velocity at each of several different concentrations of one substrate, A, holding the concentration of the other substrate, B, constant and then repeats the whole series of measurements at several different levels of B. Display of the data in a linear plotting form[1] then permits the type of distinction discussed above. The specification of formal mechanisms can also be carried to a finer level of discrimination, especially with regard to the number of kinetically significant enzyme-substrate complexes involved and the sequence in which the substrates attack. This is done by the inclusion of similar studies in the reverse direction, or in the forward direction in the presence of single products, or with the use of analogue substrates. The experimental studies considered below illustrate these applications; the original papers should be consulted for details. Quite a number of such studies are now in the literature and the value of the method is such that their numbers are virtually certain to increase rapidly. In addition to these steady-state methods based on measurements of initial velocity of chemical change, there is a technique employing the initial rate of isotope redistribution at chemical equilibrium, which can yield much the same information and sometimes an additional refinement. One study, discussed below, has used both techniques to analyze a three substrate–three product mechanism.

---

[1] Various authors prefer the different plotting forms but in principle they are all, of course, equivalent. Cleland, for example, uses the double reciprocal form to keep the variables separated, while Wong and Hanes prefer plots of v_0/A vs. A. Other workers have argued for the superiority of v_0 vs. v_0/A plots. In computer evaluation, all forms are equivalent.

GLUTAMATE-OXALACETATE TRANSAMINASE

One report that well illustrates the steady-state analytical method is that of Henson and Cleland (1) on the glutamate–oxalacetate transaminase. The formal mechanism is one of the substituted enzyme type and the reciprocal plots for each substrate at different levels of the other substrate are accordingly parallel straight lines. The reaction, which is readily reversible, showed the same character when studied in both directions. Moreover, inhibition by products was used to establish the kinetic significance of both of the possible binary complexes. The two keto acids showed strictly competitive mutual interference, and therefore generally noncompetitive behavior with respect to the amino acids, and vice versa. The occurrence of a nonproductive "dead-end" complex of the enzyme with α-ketoglutarate was also evident at high concentrations of that substrate.

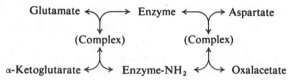

The data obtained further fulfilled the Haldane relations (equations relating the kinetic constants to the overall equilibrium constant) predicted on the basis of the substituted enzyme mechanism. These formal mechanistic conclusions from kinetic evidence are in accord with a substantial amount of other evidence relating to this enzyme.

CREATINE KINASE

An excellent study of a ternary complex mechanism has been reported by Morrison and James (2) for creatine kinase. This reaction is also a readily reversible one and the converging reciprocal plots expected for a ternary complex mechanism were obtained for all substrates in both directions. In the case of such behavior, however, it is necessary to make a further distinction regarding the relative magnitudes of the various rate constants since the converging plots could also be obtained from a Theorell–Chance mechanism. That is, converging reciprocal plots are also obtained when no ternary complex has a kinetically significant lifetime and only the two binary complexes which are the initial enzyme-substrate complexes for the two reaction directions are kinetically evident. For creatine kinase, a Theorell–Chance mechanism was eliminated as a possibility by Morrison and James on the basis of inhibition by the products in both directions. As expected for a mechanism in which all reactions are in rapid equilibrium except the interconversion of the two central ternary complexes, but as not expected for a Theorell–Chance mechanism, the apparent inhibitor constants for some of the competitive product inhibitions (nucleotide vs. nucleotide or guanidino compound vs. guanidino compound) varied with the concentration of the fixed substrate.

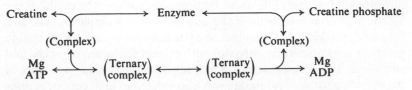

(The order of addition to form complexes is not significant.)

The product inhibition data were also inconsistent with an ordered mechanism (i.e., one in which the substrates must combine with the enzyme in an obligatory sequence) or with an ordered mechanism including the formation of dead-end complexes. Again, in this case, the mechanism indicated by the kinetic data is in accord with a variety of other evidence, including subsequent isotope exchange data (3).

RHODANESE

One further example of steady-state kinetic analysis of two-substrate mechanisms will serve to illustrate that it is not always necessary to be able to study the reaction in both directions or to make use of product inhibition. Volini and Westley (4) reported a kinetic analysis of the thiosulfate-lipoate reaction catalyzed by rhodanese, which is rendered practically irreversible by the rapid, spontaneous breakdown of the product lipoate persulfide (5). The mechanism is of the substituted enzyme variety with both of the possible binary enzyme-substrate complexes demonstrated kinetically. There is also the complication that nonproductive dead-end complexes are formed with both substrates.

The data from which this formal mechanism was inferred are illustrated schematically in Fig. 19. At low constant concentrations of either substrate, the reciprocal plots for the other substrate are linear and approach the parallel condition of the simple substituted enzyme form. As the concentration of the constant substrate is raised, it causes

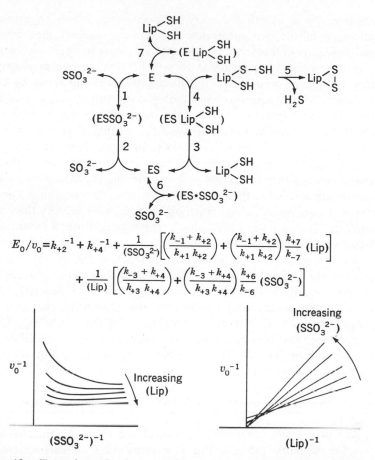

$$E_0/v_0 = k_{+2}^{-1} + k_{+4}^{-1} + \frac{1}{(SSO_3^{2-})}\left[\left(\frac{k_{-1}+k_{+2}}{k_{+1}\,k_{+2}}\right) + \left(\frac{k_{-1}+k_{+2}}{k_{+1}\,k_{+2}}\right)\frac{k_{+7}}{k_{-7}}\,(Lip)\right]$$

$$+ \frac{1}{(Lip)}\left[\left(\frac{k_{-3}+k_{+4}}{k_{+3}\,k_{+4}}\right) + \left(\frac{k_{-3}+k_{+4}}{k_{+3}\,k_{+4}}\right)\frac{k_{+6}}{k_{-6}}\,(SSO_3^{2-})\right]$$

FIG. 19. Formal mechanism, steady-state rate equation and kinetic behavior of the rhodanese-catalyzed thiosulfate-lipoate reaction. (Lip) signifies the concentration of reduced lipoate. The data shown are for the low pH range (<9), where thiosulfate inhibition predominates. Similar data were obtained in the high pH range (>10), where lipoate inhibition predominates. (Adapted from M. Volini and J. Westley, *J. Biol. Chem.*, **241**: 5168 (1966). Used by permission.)

competitive interference, distorting the plots accordingly. In plots of v_0^{-1} vs. $[B]^{-1}$, the appearance is that of substrate inhibition, with most pronounced effects at low $[A]$. The same data plotted as v_0^{-1} vs. $[A]^{-1}$, show that at higher B the effect is that of competitive inhibition superposed on the simple parallel displacement of the plots occasioned by the higher concentration of constant substrate. These kinetic data are distinctive for a substituted enzyme mechanism involving mutual interference of the two substrates. No ternary complex mechanism would yield data of this form, with or without competitive interferences.

In this work the question as to whether one or two productive binary complexes occurred in the mechanism was answered by the use of a second technique involving analogue substrates, as discussed by Wong and Hanes (6). It was clear at the outset that at least one binary complex was necessary, since otherwise the maximum velocity of the reaction would have increased without limit as the concentrations of both substrates were increased, and this was not the case.[2] When alternate sulfur donor substrates were used in the rhodanese-catalyzed reaction with cyanide as the sulfur acceptor substrate, the sulfur donor methane thiosulfonate yielded much higher maximum velocity than did thiosulfate (7). Since the sulfur-substituted enzyme formed from both substrates is identical, as are the subsequent steps in the overall reaction, this observation carried the clear implication that the breakdown of an enzyme-thiosulfate binary complex exerts a major kinetic influence on maximum velocity in the reaction involving thiosulfate. Similarly, the occurrence of a binary complex between the substituted enzyme and dihydrolipoate was shown by a comparison of maximum velocities obtained using different sulfur *acceptor* substrates, with thiosulfate as the sulfur donor (4). At pH values below 9, the maximum velocity obtained with dihydrolipoate as acceptor was substantially lower than that for cyanide, again indicating the existence of a kinetically significant complex involving the substrate with the lower maximum velocity, i.e., dihydrolipoate.

As with the other enzymes discussed above, the formal mechanism shown for rhodanese (given in Fig. 19 with its initial velocity equation, derived from the mechanism by the steady-state method) is in accord with other work on this enzyme. As mentioned in Chap. 7, the sulfur-substituted rhodanese intermediate has been isolated and the stoichiometry of its reactions with the substrates and products has been examined directly.

ISOTOPE EQUILIBRATION STUDIES

The kinetic theory for initial rates of isotope redistribution at chemical equilibrium has been treated by Boyer (8,9), Alberty and his

---

[2] Maximum velocities must be limited by the unimolecular steps in mechanisms, i.e., by decomposition of enzyme-substrate complexes. Velocities limited by bimolecular steps can always be increased by increasing the concentrations of reactants and, hence, are not maximum velocities.

associates (10), and Wong and Hanes (11). There have now been a number of applications. At the two-substrate level of complexity, Boyer and his associates have done isotope equilibration work with several enzymes for which much steady-state kinetic information is available (12–15). Morrison and Cleland (3) have done an isotope equilibration study of creatine kinase that extends the results of the steady-state study of this enzyme discussed above. Rose *et al.* (16) have also used this technique to establish a clear inference of substituted enzyme mechanism for muscle aldolase. Dalziel and Dickinson (17) have done a particularly elegant study of both the steady state and isotope equilibration behavior of liver alcohol dehydrogenase. With secondary alcohols, the breakdown of the ternary complex with enzyme and coenzyme limits the maximum velocity. With primary alcohols, the ternary complex reacts so rapidly that the steady-state behavior is that of the Theorell–Chance mechanism, and isotope exchange data confirm this view. The particular example discussed in the last section of this chapter involves a three-substrate, three-product enzyme, where the results are of special interest because no really exhaustive steady-state treatment for mechanisms of this complexity has been published. Thus, the isotope equilibration results, consistent with the results of a steady-state analysis, are important in bolstering confidence in the inferred mechanism.

The isotope equilibration method as originated by Boyer is based on an analysis of the events that occur when a tracer amount of highly labeled substrate is added to an enzyme-catalyzed reaction that is already at equilibrium. The concentrations of substrates and products do not change, of course, and the observations made are of the initial velocities of appearance of the tracer isotope in products. The system has the advantage that working at chemical equilibrium simplifies the theoretical treatment and also makes less troublesome the considerations involved where the solvent takes part in the reaction. The evidence obtained is not fundamentally different in principle from that obtained from conventional initial velocity work, as has been pointed out by Alberty *et al.* (10), but some information is obtainable this way that is otherwise inaccessible by steady-state studies.[3]

Three main areas of application to ternary (or quanternary) complex mechanisms have had practical importance. Each of these applications makes good sense intuitively, as well as proving out in rigorous derivation. The technique can be a very sensitive test for

[3] Some further consideration of isotope equilibration studies occurs in Chap. 10. See also the first general reference of the present chapter.

distinguishing purely random sequence mechanisms from those that involve some degree of order preference. In random mechanisms, all isotope exchange rates are expected to increase to maximum values as the concentration of any substrate is increased unless dead-end complexes are formed. This is in contrast to ordered mechanisms, where some exchange rates are expected to increase and then decrease as the concentrations of some of the substrates are increased.

The second application derives from the first since it is all the substrates other than the last in an ordered mechanism that show the biphasic behavior characteristic of ordered mechanisms in this system. For the last substrate the behavior is like that of all substrates in the random mechanism, simple increase to a maximum value. This of course provides a means for distinguishing which substrate is last in an ordered mechanism, supplementing the methods for this purpose discussed in Chap. 8.

The third application addresses the question of the rate-limiting step at maximum velocity. In ternary (or quaternary) complex mechanisms this concerns the possibility that the step limiting the maximum rate may be the interconversion of the enzyme-bound substrates and products, i.e., interconversion of the ternary (or quaternary) enzyme-substrate complex and the corresponding enzyme-product complex. Where this possibility is realized (i.e., the rapid equilibrium random case discussed in Chap. 8), it is expected that exchange rates for all labeled substrates and products will be identical at maximum velocity. If the rate limitation involves primarily other steps, however, large differences are expected.

FORMYLTETRAHYDROFOLATE SYNTHETASE

Joyce and Himes have studied the kinetics of the reaction catalyzed by formyltetrahydrofolate synthetase by both the steady-state methods of Cleland (18) and the isotope equilibration method (19). The steady-state studies yielded the results expected for a random sequence of addition of the three substrates to form a quaternary complex. The analysis was somewhat complicated by the occurrence of some dead-end complexes but this phenomenon caused no ambiguities in the interpretation. As expected for the random sequence mechanism, all the isotope exchange rates increased to maximum values as the concentrations of variable substrates were increased at chemical equilibrium.

Moreover, the different exchange rates at saturating reactant concentrations were unequal, indicating that interconversion of the quaternary complexes was not simply rate limiting at maximum velocity. The absence of *large* differences among these exchange rates, however, suggested that the rate of interconversion of the quaternary complexes and the rates of dissociation of reactants from the enzyme were of the same order of magnitude. The picture that emerges from this study, then, is of a mechanism involving obligatory formation of a quaternary complex in either direction, with random order of addition of substrates, in which the maximum velocity is not simply dominated by any one step.

It would be possible to cite many more applications of modern enzyme kinetics. For those with a particular interest in this field, the fine studies of Hersh and Jencks on coenzyme A transferase (20) and of Ray *et al.* on phosphoglucomutase (21) are recommended reading.

GENERAL REFERENCES

Cleland, W. W.: *Ann. Rev. Biochem.*, **36**: (1967).
Rose, I. A.: *Ann. Rev. Biochem.*, **35**: (1966).

SPECIFIC REFERENCES

1. Henson, C. P., and W. W. Cleland: *Biochemistry*, **3**: 338 (1964).
2. Morrison, J. F., and E. James: *Biochem. J.*, **97**: 37 (1965).
3. Morrison, J. F., and W. W. Cleland: *J. Biol. Chem.*, **241**: 673 (1966).
4. Volini, M., and J. Westley: *J. Biol. Chem.*, **241**; 5168 (1966).
5. Villarejo, M., and J. Westley: *J. Biol. Chem.*, **238**; 4016 (1963).
6. Wong, J. T., and C. S. Hanes: *Canad. J. Biochem. Physiol.*, **40**: 763 (1962).
7. Mintel, R., and J. Westley: *J. Biol. Chem.*, **241**: 3381 (1966).
8. Boyer, P. D.: *Arch. Biochem. Biophys.*, **82**: 387 (1959).
9. Boyer, P. D., and E. Silverstein: *Acta Chem. Scand.*, **17**, Suppl. 1, 195 (1963).
10. Alberty, R. A., V. Bloomfield, L. Peller, and E. L. King: *J. Am. Chem. Soc.*, **84**: 4381 (1962).
11. Wong, J. T., and C. S. Hanes: *Nature*, **203**: 492 (1964).
12. Fromm, H. J., E. Silverstein, and P. D. Boyer: *J. Biol. Chem.*, **239**: 3645 (1964).
13. Silverstein, E., and P. D. Boyer: *J. Biol. Chem.*, **239**: 3901 (1964).
14. Silverstein, E., and P. D. Boyer: *J. Biol. Chem.*, **239**: 3908 (1964).
15. Graves, D. J., and P. D. Boyer: *Biochemistry*, **1**: 739 (1962).

16. Rose, I. A., E. L. O'Connell, and A. Mehler: *J. Biol. Chem.*, **240**: 1758 (1965).
17. Dalziel, K., and F. M. Dickinson: *Biochem. J.*, **100**: 34 (1966)
18. Joyce, B. K., and R. H. Himes: *J. Biol. Chem.*, **241**: 5725 (1966).
19. Joyce, B. K., and R. H. Himes: *J. Biol. Chem.*, **241**: 5716 (1966).
20. Hersh, L. B., and W. P. Jencks: *J. Biol. Chem.*, **242**: 3468 (1967).
21. Ray, W. J., Jr., G. Roscelli, and D. S. Kirkpatrick: *J. Biol. Chem.*, **241**: 2603 (1966).

PART

THE PARTICULARS OF ENZYME MECHANISMS

The considerations of Part I of this book concluded with the idea that an adequate theoretical framework for explaining enzymic catalysis exists. Next required was a general approach for analyzing enzyme mechanisms into their individual component reactions; Part II has provided such an approach. It remains, then, to find means for determining the rate constants for the individual reactions and for identifying the particular enzymic groups involved in the catalysis. If particular roles consistent with the principles and facts of physical organic chemistry can then be assigned to these groups to account for the magnitudes of the observed rate constants, enzymic catalysis will be largely understood, at least at one level of resolution. The following chapters discuss the steady-state and pre-steady-state means available for determining constants and the methods used for implicating particular groups. It is strongly stressed, however, that work along these lines for any enzyme is not likely to prove very illuminating without prior or concomitant determination of the formal mechanism. To determine the value of any kinetic parameter without also determining the reaction or composite of reactions to which it applies is less than maximally helpful.

To be quite explicit, this organization of the material is intended to constitute a recommendation of strategy for work on enzyme mechanisms. A rational approach to such research is first to determine the formal mechanism, as discussed in Part II. With this as a basis for isolating the component reactions, individual rate and equilibrium constants can be examined under a variety of conditions. As we shall see in the chapters that follow, such quantitative data can lead to the assignment of specific catalytic roles to known chemical features of the enzyme.

10

RATE AND EQUILIBRIUM CONSTANTS FROM STEADY-STATE VELOCITY AND ISOTOPE EQUILIBRATION STUDIES

It will be noted that formal kinetic work of the kinds discussed in Chap. 9 is capable of yielding values for some of the individual rate constants for unimolecular steps and equilibrium constants for some of the bimolecular steps in an enzyme mechanism. Moreover, it is sometimes possible to obtain from steady-state studies enough information about the *relative* magnitudes of individual rate constants to permit some useful approximations, as when equilibrium among enzymic forms obtains and $K_m \simeq K_s$. In what follows, we shall consider the strategy and tactics useful for these purposes. Subsequent chapters then deal with the uses of these constants in detecting important enzymic functional groups and assigning them roles in the catalysis.

SECONDARY PLOTS FROM TWO-SUBSTRATE STUDIES

One of the two most general steady-state ways to evaluate the constants in a mechanism is by means of secondary kinetic plots. Any one reciprocal plot of data for a two-substrate mechanism will in general yield only apparent constants (i.e., kinetic coefficients dependent on the concentration of the nonvaried substrate). However, the apparent K_m and V values from a series of plots from different constant substrate concentrations can themselves be expressed in slope-intercept forms and so plotted and extrapolated to yield concentration-independent kinetic coefficients whose composition in terms of rate constants is known if the formal mechanism has been elucidated.[1]

---

[1] As pointed out in several places in earlier chapters, the fact that multiple forms of the transient complexes may occur in all mechanisms does not invalidate the considerations that follow. That the rate constants evaluated may in fact be composite constants means only that the values obtained are lower limit values for the true individual rate constants.

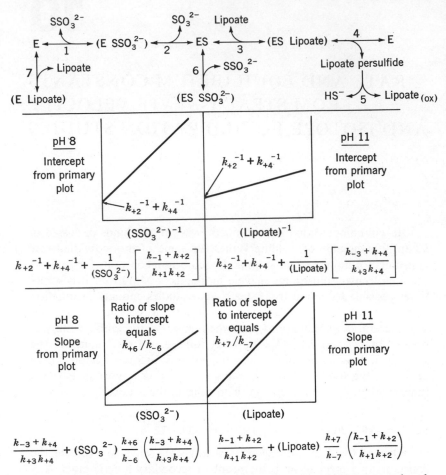

FIG. 20. Secondary plots of kinetic data for the rhodanese-catalyzed thiosulfate-lipoate reaction. Slope and intercept values were taken from double reciprocal plots such as those in Fig. 19 and replotted. The expressions for the slope and intercept terms were taken from the steady-state rate equation (Fig. 19) for the formal mechanism shown. (Adapted from M. Volini and J. Westley, *J. Biol. Chem.*, **241**: 5168 (1966). Used by permission.)

Some secondary plots for the rhodanese data referred to in Chap. 9 are shown in Fig. 20 along with their slope-intercept equations and the overall reaction sequence (1). Such plots permitted evaluation of $(k_{+2}^{-1} + k_{+4}^{-1})$, $[(k_{-1} + k_{+2})/k_{+1}]$, and $[(k_{-3} + k_{+4})/k_{+3}]$. Separate determination of k_{+2} and of the relative values of k_{+2} and k_{-1}, by means described below, then permitted k_{+4} and k_{-1}/k_{+1} to be obtained.

Values for the dead-end inhibitor constants k_{+6}/k_{-6} and k_{+7}/k_{-7} were obtained in the same study by evaluation as competitive inhibitor constants. In this way, from initial velocity measurements in one direction only plus a small amount of ancillary kinetic information obtained using alternate substrates, it was possible to evaluate both unimolecular rate constants for that direction and all but one of the equilibrium constants for the bimolecular steps. This reaction cannot be studied in the reverse direction as it is essentially irreversible.

INITIAL VELOCITY STUDIES IN BOTH DIRECTIONS

Where steady-state kinetic studies can be made in both directions in the absence and in the presence of single products, the second general steady-state method for obtaining constants may be used. The systematic analysis of two-substrate mechanisms following the methods outlined in the previous chapter is capable of yielding such information; equilibrium constants for all of the steps can be obtained. A key principle is that the inhibitor constants for products in product inhibition can be true equilibrium constants.[2] Examples of this kind of study are the analyses of the creatine kinase ternary complex mechanism (2) and the transaminase substituted-enzyme mechanism (3), referred to in Chap. 9.

Taking the latter case, it is easy to see the basis for the determination.

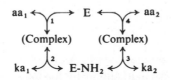

Initial rate studies with aa_1 and ka_2 as substrates permitted determination of K_2 in the presence of ka_1, which must inhibit competitively with respect to ka_2, and of K_4 in the presence of aa_2, which must inhibit competitively with respect to aa_1. Similarly, K_3 and K_1 could be determined in experiments with aa_2 and ka_1 as substrates and aa_1 and ka_2, separately, as inhibitors. The complication of a dead-end complex between one of the ka's and the free enzyme did not seriously interfere with the analysis.

---

[2] In the transaminase mechanism for example, where the first product is competitive with the second substrate, the competitive inhibition constant is a true equilibrium constant. Holding the first substrate at saturating concentration imposes a dead-end-like situation on the inhibition.

In most such cases, however, it does not appear that any individual rate constants were sought and obtained. With the equilibrium constants now known, employment of some of the means discussed below for determining any of the individual unimolecular rate constants in these mechanisms would permit simple calculation of the individual bimolecular rate constants for the corresponding reverse reactions as well. In principle, then, steady-state studies conducted in both directions are capable of yielding values for many of the individual rate constants in the productive pathways of the mechanism, bimolecular constants being calculated as the ratios of the appropriate equilibrium constants and the unimolecular rate constants for the reactions in the reverse direction. The chief requirement for a relatively complete analysis will be: (a) the application of modern steady-state kinetic methods for evaluating all of the equilibrium constants, (b) the employment of any or all of the methods discussed below for evaluating individual unimolecular rate constants, and (c) preferably a mechanism that can be studied in both directions. The only alternative to such a program, alone or in combination with the isotope equilibration studies introduced in Chap. 9 and discussed further below, is the approach through pre-steady-state kinetics, to be considered in Chap. 11. These various approaches should find frequent application together in studies for evaluating rate constants in complex mechanisms.

THE USE OF ALTERNATE SUBSTRATES TO DETECT RATE-DETERMINING STEPS

In Chap. 9 two different applications of analogue substrates were dealt with: (a) their use in distinguishing which is the first substrate in a ternary complex mechanism and (b) their use in detecting kinetically significant intermediates. A third usage is related to the latter in that quantitative handling of the same data may yield a value for one of the unimolecular rate constants.

Consider the case of the substituted enzyme mechanism:

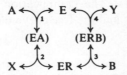

Here the initial velocity under conditions of saturation with both substrates A and B must be determined by the unimolecular rate constants k_{+2} and k_{+4}. In fact

$$E_0/V = \left(\frac{1}{k_{+2}} + \frac{1}{k_{+4}}\right)^{-1}$$

for such a mechanism. Then if it can be shown that, for example, several A analogue substrates yield different values of V while several B substrates do not alter V, it is clear that k_{+2} is so small that it dominates V and in fact $V \simeq k_{+2}E_0$. Furthermore, when there is a series of A substrates but only a single B substrate available, the analysis can still be made if the A series is extensive enough so that V approaches a limiting maximum value governed by k_{+4}. Alternatively, if the chemistry of the event in the k_{+2} step can lead to quantitative predictions as to how that rate constant should vary for different A's, a conclusion may still be reached. In such cases the value of k_{+2} can be established from V for the "slower" members of the A series and that of k_{+4} either directly from the limiting V with the faster members of the A series or by difference from any V in which it is a significant term. Note also that the symmetry of the substituted enzyme mechanism ensures that exactly similar reasoning can be applied to cases that are the reverse of the example taken above, i.e., in which $k_{+4} \ll k_{+2}$ and where either both series or only a B series may be available. The same kind of approach can be fruitful, moreover, when applied to ternary complex mechanisms. There the distinction between the ordered mechanism with a kinetically significant ternary complex and that without (the Theorell–Chance mechanism) can be made using alternate substrates.[3]

An example of such an analysis of a substituted enzyme mechanism is in the kinetic work on rhodanese mentioned earlier. There, with cyanide as B substrate, thiosulfate and the aliphatic and aromatic thiosulfonates formed an A series in which there was a nearly hundred-fold increase in V between thiosulfate and methane thiosulfonate with a leveling off of V in the reactive aromatic series (4). From these data, k_{+2} is seen to dominate the V with thiosulfate as substrate. When in subsequent work (1) lipoate was used as B substrate, and thiosulfate as A substrate, both unimolecular rate constants were significant in V, and prior knowledge of k_{+2} permitted calculation of k_{+4} from the above relationships.

---

[3] If breakdown of the ternary complex is a kinetically significant event (i.e., if k_{+3} is not much greater than k_{+4} in Fig. 18a of Chap. 8), different substrates will in general have different maximum velocities. If, however, the rate constant for breakdown of the ternary complex is large relative to that for dissociation of the subsequent binary complex, structure of the substrate related to the first product may not influence the maximum velocity. The fact that various primary alcohols yield the same maximum velocity with alcohol dehydrogenase, for example, strongly suggests that the mechanism is of the Theorell–Chance variety, with breakdown of the enzyme-NADH complex rate-limiting at maximum velocity.

It should also be noted that in such work the occurrence of "slow" substrates raises a further possibility for analysis. With many enzymes one or more substrates are essentially at equilibrium with their enzyme-bound forms, i.e., the two-substrate analogue of the original Henri equilibrium assumption is partly or wholly fulfilled. Full-scale two-substrate studies in both directions, with product inhibition, are capable of distinguishing such cases as both K_m values as well as both equilibrium constants are obtained. However, unidirectional studies must again rely on analogue substrate behavior to detect those cases in which K_m values are essentially equilibrium constants.

Both types of studies have already been mentioned. The creatine kinase work, for example, showed that all of the substrates and products (i.e., all of the substrates in both directions) are essentially in equilibrium with the enzymic forms (2). Also in the case of the transaminase discussed previously, the Michaelis constants and product inhibition (equilibrium) constants coincide for the amino acid substrates, although not for the keto acid substrates. In the rhodanese work, however, where studies could be made in one direction only, it was the use of analogue substrates that permitted the conclusion that $K_m^{SSO_3^{2-}} \simeq k_{-1}/k_{+1}$. Here the inference was based on the finding that the nearly hundredfold increase obtained in k_{+2} on replacing thiosulfate by methane thiosulfonate as substrate was not accompanied by a corresponding difference in K_m (4). The correctness of the conclusion then depends on the assumption that a compensating increase had not occurred in k_{+1}. In this particular case, since it is known that there is a cationic site for the anionic thiosulfate substrate (5) and since the thiosulfonate has a smaller charge than thiosulfate, the assumption has experimental justification.

Finally, note that the principle used here could be extended to any case in which V and K_m for analogue substrates vary in direct proportion. Such a case might occur, for example, in a reaction in which both the A and B substrate are "fast," i.e., in which both k_{+2} and k_{+4} are large. Under such circumstances, it could occur that k_{-1} would not be a significant term in K_m and k_{+2} might then dominate both $K_m \simeq k_{+2}/k_{+1}$ and $V \simeq k_{+2} E_0$. Carboxypeptidase seems to represent such a case. This situation is not likely to be met frequently, however, as it requires that $k_{-1} \ll k_{+2} \ll k_{+4}$.

NONCOMPETITIVE EFFECTS; THE ASCORBATE OXIDASE MECHANISM

One further aid is available to the steady-state kineticist who wishes to interpret his data in terms of rate and equilibrium constants. It happens sometimes that pure noncompetitive effects are observed, i.e., that V is altered without changing K_m. When the effect is occasioned by changing substrates, the interpretation can sometimes be made that equilibrium conditions prevail for the slowest substrate, as in the preceding section. Further, where the effect occurs as a result of adding a modifier, a similar argument has sometimes been employed.

Simple noncompetitive behavior of a modifier in a one-substrate system was shown by Morales (7) to require either equilibrium conditions or steric blockage of one of the two routes of formation of the ternary enzyme-substrate-modifier complex.[4] For one substrate–one product kinetics, then, *activation* effects on V that did not alter K_m have been taken as evidence that $K_m \simeq K_s$ in the absence of the activator. Similarly, effects of pH on V in the absence of corresponding changes in K_m have been considered indicative of equilibrium, since the hydronium ion is so small that a steric blockage was considered rather unlikely.

Four points regarding this interpretation of noncompetitive behavior required attention. First it is emphasized that a single instance of noncompetitive behavior is not a strong basis for concluding that equilibrium exists even in a single substrate system uncomplicated by the suspicion of aggregation–disaggregation or other major conformational changes in the enzyme. For any one case, in the absence of evidence to the contrary, the change in k_{+2} could be approximately balanced in K_m by a change in k_{+1}, i.e., by coincidental effects of the modifier on the two constants. The case is strengthened, however, if more than one modifier gives a noncompetitive effect, especially if the modifiers are chemically diverse.

In studies of ascorbate oxidase, for example, the interpretation of noncompetitive pH effects has been facilitated by the discovery of a noncompetitive activation by halide ions. Treatment of the enzyme in its reduced form with chloride under some circumstances can increase V by several hundred percent with affecting $K_m^{\mathrm{ascorbate}}$ (8). With both a noncompetitive pH effect and a noncompetitive activation, equilibrium among the enzymic forms is a distinct possibility.

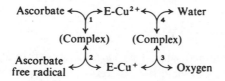

The second point for emphasis concerns the possibility of conformation changes, including aggregation–disaggregation, as a cause of noncompetitive behavior. As a simple example one may envision an

[4] See Chap. 4.

enzyme composed of n subunits dissociable by changing the pH. If the separate subunits had enzymic activity but aggregation was such that only one subunit in each aggregate were active, noncompetitive pH effects could be seen. Essentially, change of pH in the direction causing dissociation could increase V up to n-fold just as adding more enzyme could, without affecting K_m. The example taken is deliberately very gross to indicate the possibility of noncompetitive behavior from causes other than equilibrium even where activation is involved or even where a modifier as small as the hydronium ion is involved. Especially since one might expect in practice to encounter rather more subtle conformation changes, efforts must be made to distinguish whether noncompetitive effects involve changes in the physical properties of the protein before concluding that the cause is equilibrium. In the case of ascorbate oxidase mentioned above, for example, the sedimentation and gel filtration behavior and the fluorescence spectra of the enzyme were examined for clues to the cause of chloride activation phenomenon. No disaggregation or conformational changes detectable by these means were involved, again leaving open the possibility that $K_m^{ascorbate} \simeq K_s^{ascorbate}$

The third point to be made regarding noncompetitive behavior relates to the validity of applying one-substrate criteria to two-substrate systems. One may certainly wonder whether simply holding one substrate at saturating concentration is sufficient to permit analysis of such inhibitor data as a pseudo-one-substrate case. The question has been considered carefully in principle (9,10). Here, we shall follow the practice of taking up an example rather than embarking on the most general treatment, as this seems a more apt way to gain an intuitive grasp of what is involved.

Consider the mechanism shown in Fig. 17, Chap. 8. This is the substituted enzyme form, of which the transaminase, rhodanese, and ascorbate oxidase mentioned earlier are examples. One reciprocal form of the steady-state rate equation for initial velocities with this mechanism is

$$\frac{E_0}{v_0} = \left(\frac{k_{-1}+k_{+2}}{k_{+1}k_{+2}}\right)A^{-1} + \left(\frac{k_{-3}+k_{+4}}{k_{+3}k_{+4}}\right)B^{-1} + \left(\frac{k_{+2}+k_{+4}}{k_{+2}k_{+4}}\right)$$

Kinetic data obtained with A as variable substrate at saturating concentrations of B, will yield the last term in the equation as the ratio of E_0 to maximum velocity. The experimentally defined K_m^A (the negative inverse abscissal intercept, or ratio of slope to ordinate intercept, of the double reciprocal plot) under such conditions will equal

$$\frac{k_{+4}(k_{-1}+k_{+2})}{k_{+1}(k_{+2}+k_{+4})}$$

TABLE 4. *Kinetic Coefficients in a Substituted Enzyme Mechanism*

Variable Substrate	General Case		$k_{+2} \ll k_{+4}$		$k_{+4} \ll k_{+2}$	
	K_m	V/E_0	K_m	V/E_0	K_m	V/E_0
A	$\dfrac{k_{+4}(k_{-1}+k_{+2})}{k_{+1}(k_{+2}+k_{+4})}$	$\dfrac{k_{+2}k_{+4}}{k_{+2}+k_{+4}}$	$\dfrac{k_{-1}+k_{+2}}{k_{+1}}$	k_{+2}	Varies linearly with k_{+4}	k_{+4}
B	$\dfrac{k_{+2}(k_{-3}+k_{+4})}{k_{+3}(k_{+2}+k_{+4})}$	$\dfrac{k_{+2}k_{+4}}{k_{+2}+k_{+4}}$	Varies linearly with k_{+2}	k_{+2}	$\dfrac{k_{-3}+k_{+4}}{k_{+3}}$	k_{+4}

The expression where B is the variable substrate has the same form (Table 4). This formulation is entirely general for this style of mechanism.

Consider now the possibility of noncompetitive effects. To take a particular case, let us examine what kinds of modifiers could alter V without changing K_m^A. This will be easy if we first tabulate the forms of these coefficients under various conditions.

Inspection of Table 4 leads to several conclusions regarding the possibility of affecting V without changing K_m^A.

1. No alteration of k_{+3} or k_{-3} can affect either V or K_m^A.

2. No alteration of k_{+1} or k_{-1} can affect V.

3. *Any* alteration of k_{+4} must affect V and K_m^A in the same proportion, i.e., must look *un*competitive for A.

From the foregoing conclusions, it follows that if any simple noncompetitive effect (for A) involving alteration at a single step in the mechanism is possible, it must surely involve the k_{+2} step.

4. Alteration of k_{+2} poses two possibilities:

   a. Where $k_{+4} \ll k_{+2}$, the effects must look *competitive* for A if effects are seen at all.

   b. Where $k_{+2} \ll k_{+4}$, mixed inhibition will be seen for A in general (both V and K_m^A changing). However, where and only where k_{+2} is also $\ll k_{-1}$, strictly noncompetitive[5] behavior will be obtained.

In short, for mechanisms of this kind, the simplest inhibitor or activator condition yielding noncompetitive effects with respect to A

---

[5] The reader is reminded that our use of this term means intersection of the reciprocal plots on the abscissa.

is that involving both equilibrium in step 1 and k_{+2} as the site of modifier action. While various coincidental circumstances could also yield this result, including coincidence of k_{-1} and k_{+4} or balancing alterations in several rate constants at once, occurrence of strictly noncompetitive behavior with diverse agents suggests the simpler explanation.

Application of the above analysis to the ascorbate oxidase data showing noncompetitive pH effects and activation of V without effects on K_m^A seems to affirm the indications mentioned earlier; i.e., on this basis equilibrium between the enzyme and ascorbate may well obtain and k_{+2} may well be substantially smaller than k_{+4}.

The fourth point to be made concerning such interpretations, however, suggests caution in reaching these conclusions, for activation, like pH effects, should not in fact be exempted from considerations of steric blockage. Activation may be only the removal of a blocking group, be it a bound inhibitor or an enzymic group, that blocks the active site, preventing both binding and reaction of a substrate. Noncompetitive behavior could easily have such a basis, especially in cases like ascorbate oxidase, where the active site involves a metal ion that is an essential catalytic group as well as a major binding group. In such a case, a ligand for the enzymic copper ion might well be a non-competitive inhibitor; another ligand, displacing the first, could be a noncompetitive activator. These considerations do not change the *kinetic* interpretation but bear on the chemical conclusions to be drawn.

The case for ascorbate oxidase is thus ambiguous in the absence of additional data. Two principal approaches have provided further information: studies with analogue substrates, and direct measurements of some rate constants. Yamazaki and Piette (11) found that the maximum velocity of the ascorbate oxidase-catalyzed reaction was identical for ascorbic acid and reductic acid as substrates. Except by chance coincidence of k_{+2} values for these compounds, it follows that k_{+4} rather than k_{+2} limited the maximum velocity. Subsequent studies, however, showed that at pH values where these two substrates are both fully ionized (the monoanion being the active form of the substrate) the maximum velocities differed by a factor of ten, suggesting that the earlier result was for circumstances where the k_{+2} values for the two substrates were coincidentally the same (8). Furthermore, direct measurements of velocity constants have shown that the oxidation of reduced ascorbate oxidase is very rapid while its reduction by ascorbate is relatively slow (12). Although none of this evidence definitely rules out the possibility that entire new sites are covered or uncovered in the pH and activation effects, the combined impact of the data is the suggestion that noncompetitive behavior in this case may be based on equilibrium among enzymic forms and rate limitation by k_{+2}. Clearly, further kinetic work on ascorbic oxidase is in order.

ISOTOPE EQUILIBRATION STUDIES

In Chap. 9 reference was made to the uses of isotope equilibration methods worked out by Boyer (13) for delineating formal ternary complex mechanisms. The technique involves measuring the initial velocity of isotope redistribution in an enzyme-catalyzed reaction that is at chemical equilibrium before the tracer is added. Here we wish to present a specific development of this kind of method for securing values of some individual rate constants in certain substituted enzyme mechanisms.[6]

Many substituted enzyme mechanisms contain sequences of the form

$$E + A \underset{k_{-1}}{\overset{k_{+1}}{\rightleftharpoons}} (EA) \underset{k_{-2}}{\overset{k_{+2}}{\rightleftharpoons}} X + E'$$

where E' is the substituted enzyme. Where E and E' are sufficiently stable, this system may be obtained at chemical equilibrium simply by omitting the second substrate from the overall enzyme-catalyzed reaction. If a tracer amount of labeled A is introduced into such an equilibrium system, (EA) at the steady state will be the sum of two terms: $(EA)_a$, the concentration of the labeled form and $(EA)_x$, the concentration of the unlabeled form. When we refer to the situation where the isotopic label in A is such that it appears in X, rather than in E', we can speak of the initial rate of appearance in X of the label from A. This rate, $\mathbf{R}$, must be equal to $k_{+2}(EA)_a$ and the following equations define the equilibria in the individual steps:

$$E = \frac{(EA)_a + (EA)_x}{K_1 A}$$
$$E' = \frac{K_2[(EA)_a + (EA)_x]}{X}$$

The enzyme conservation equation is

$$E_0 = E + (EA)_a + (EA)_x + E'$$

and substitution from the equilibrium equations yields

$$E_0 = [(EA)_a + (EA)_x]\left(1 + \frac{1}{K_1 A} + \frac{K_2}{X}\right)$$

---

[6] The derivation given here was pointed out to the author by S. J. Davidson. Cleland has considered this system in a somewhat different form (14).

With these fundamental relations as a description of the system, we can then make the steady-state assumption for the initial velocity of isotope redistribution in the system and secure some useful relationships.

$$\frac{d(EA)_a}{dt} = k_{+1}AE - (EA)_a(k_{-1} + k_{+2}) = 0 \qquad \text{at the steady state}$$

This equation simplifies to $k_{-1}(EA)_x = k_{+2}(EA)_a$. The enzyme conservation equation can then be written as

$$E_0 = (EA)_a\left(\frac{k_{+2}}{k_{-1}} + 1\right)\left(1 + \frac{1}{K_1A} + \frac{K_2}{X}\right)$$

from which

$$(EA)_a = \frac{k_{-1}E_0}{(k_{-1} + k_{+2})\left(1 + \frac{1}{K_1A} + \frac{K_2}{X}\right)}$$

The label equilibration rate $\mathbf{R}$, which equals $k_{+2}(EA)_a$, is thus related to the kinetic parameters as follows:

$$\mathbf{R} = \frac{k_{-1}k_{+2}E_0}{(k_{-1} + k_{+2})\left(1 + \frac{1}{K_1A} + \frac{K_2}{X}\right)} \qquad (45)$$

This equation clearly implies that at sufficient concentrations of A and X, the label equilibration rate will be independent of those concentrations, approaching the value

$$\frac{k_{-1}k_{+2}E_0}{k_{-1} + k_{+2}} = \mathbf{R}_{\max}$$

Since k_{+2} can often be evaluated independently, from conventional steady-state velocity measurements, determination of $\mathbf{R}_{\max}$ (conditions of saturation with both A and X) can yield the value of k_{-1} directly, and both k_{+1} and k_{-2} can be obtained from measurements at lower A and X concentrations, respectively. Furthermore, even if measurements cannot be secured when both A and X are saturating, the value of $\mathbf{R}$ as a function of the concentration of the nonsaturating reactant can still yield k_{+1}, k_{-1}, and k_{-2} if only k_{+2} is known independently.

Since the substituted enzyme form is entirely symmetrical, an exactly similar analysis can be made for the other substrate-product pair. It should be noted that experimental systems of this kind are very like their conventional steady-state velocity counterparts, requiring substrate concentrations much greater than enzyme concentrations and permitting adjustment of velocities to a convenient time scale by adjustment of enzyme concentration.

TABLE 5. *Initial Velocity of Isotope Equilibration in Substituted Enzyme Half Reaction*

	Slope	Intercept	Slope/Intercept at High A
Plot of R^{-1} vs. X^{-1}	$\dfrac{K_2(k_{-1}+k_{+2})}{k_{-1}k_{+2}E_0} = \dfrac{K_2}{R_{max}{}^a}$	$\dfrac{k_{-1}+k_{+2}}{k_{-1}k_{+2}E_0}\left(\dfrac{1}{K_1A}+1\right)$	K_2

	Slope	Intercept	Slope/Intercept at High X
Plot of R^{-1} vs. A^{-1}	$\dfrac{k_{-1}+k_{+2}}{K_1k_{-1}k_{+2}E_0} = (K_1R_{max})^{-1}$	$\dfrac{k_{-1}+k_{+2}}{k_{-1}k_{+2}E_0}\left(\dfrac{K_2}{X}+1\right)$	K_1^{-1}

^{a} $R_{max} \equiv \dfrac{k_{-1}k_{+2}E_0}{k_{-1}+k_{+2}}$. Prior knowledge of k_{+2} permits calculation of k_{-2} from K_2 and of k_{-1} from R_{max}. Then $K_1k_{-1}=k_{+1}$ and all of the constants have been obtained.

Equation (46) is a linear plotting form of Eq. (45) permitting such evaluation. Table 5 indicates the values of the slopes and intercepts of the appropriate plots.

$$R^{-1} = \frac{k_{-1}+k_{+2}}{k_{-1}k_{+2}E_0}\left(1+\frac{1}{K_1A}+\frac{K_2}{X}\right) \tag{46}$$

This technique has great promise for systematic determination of the equilibrium constants and, as always, with the caution necessitated by the probable presence of multiple transient complexes, the rate constants in enzyme-catalyzed reactions.

GENERAL REFERENCES

Cleland, W. W.: *Ann. Rev. Biochem.*, **36**: (1967).
Rose, I. A.: *Ann. Rev. Biochem.*, **35**: (1966).

SPECIFIC REFERENCES

1. Volini, M., and J. Westley: *J. Biol. Chem.*, **241**: 5168 (1966).
2. Morrison, J. F., and E. James: *Biochem. J.*, **97**: 37 (1965).
3. Henson, C. P., and W. W. Cleland: *Biochemistry*, **3**: 338 (1964).
4. Mintel, R., and J. Westley: *J. Biol. Chem.*, **241**: 3381 (1966).
5. Mintel, R., and J. Westley, *J. Biol. Chem.*, **241**: 3386 (1966).
6. Lumry, R., and E. L. Smith: *Discussions Faraday Soc.*, **20**: 105 (1955).

7. Morales, M. F.: *J. Am. Chem. Soc.*, **77**: 4169 (1955).
8. Gerwin, B. R., and J. Westley: Manuscript in preparation.
9. Hearn, J., S. Bernhard, S. Friess, D. Botts, and M. Morales: in P. D. Boyer, H. A. Lardy, and K. Myrbäck (eds.), *The Enzymes*, 2nd ed., Vol. 1, Academic, New York, 1959, p. 89.
10. Walter, C.: *Enzyme Kinetics*, The Ronald Press, New York, 1966, pp. 50–52.
11. Yamazaki, I., and L. H. Piette: *Biochim. Biophys. Acta*, **50**: 62 (1961).
12. Nakamura, T., and Y. Ogura, *Symp. Abstr., Seventh Intern. Congr. Biochem., Tokyo*, **1**; 189 (1967).
13. Boyer, P. D.: *Arch. Biochem. Biophys.*, **82**: 387 (1959).
14. Cleland, W. W.: *Ann. Rev. Biochem.*, **36**: 77 (1967).

11

RATE CONSTANTS
FROM PRE-STEADY-STATE STUDIES

Besides the steady-state methods treated in Chap. 10, there are other procedures that can yield quantitative data of value in characterizing the reactions that comprise an enzyme mechanism. These are the methods that deal with the direct measurement of rates in enzyme-catalyzed reactions under circumstances where the property observed does not reflect the overall steady state. This category includes the study of the transient pre-steady-state phase of reactions, utilizing extraordinary equipment to resolve events on a scale of milli- or micro-seconds.

THE TRANSIENT PHASE

Before examining the methods involved in pre-steady-state determinations, it is necessary to take note of the detailed time course of the enzyme-catalyzed reaction. We already have developed suitable differential equations describing the steady-state situation for the one-substrate mechanism. Integrated forms of these equations yield time course curves for the steady state.[1]

For initial velocities in the absence of product and where $A \gg E$,

$$\frac{d(EA)}{dt} = k_{+1}A_0[E_0 - (EA)] - (EA)[k_{-1} + k_{+2}] \tag{47}$$

and

$$\frac{dX}{dt} = k_{+2}(EA) \tag{48}$$

[1] This development can be done in several different ways (1,2). The treatment presented here derives mainly from that of Laidler (3).

Application of the steady-state approximation to Eq. (47), gives

$$(EA)_0 = \frac{k_{+1}A_0 E_0}{k_{-1} + k_{+2} + k_{+1}A_0} = \frac{A_0 E_0}{K_m + A_0} \tag{49}$$

This is the hypothetical concentration of (EA) at zero time under the steady-state assumption. It is the steady-state level assumed for initial velocity in conventional steady-state analysis (Fig. 21). Indeed, during the time after the steady state has been reached but before much product has accumulated, $(EA)_0$ equals (EA) to a very good approximation. After that time, dropping the subscript zero from (EA) and replacing A_0 by $(A_0 - X)$ provides a general equation for (EA) during the whole steady state if $A_0 \gg E_0$. For the time *before* the steady state is achieved, Eq. (47) can be integrated to yield a nonsteady-state expression for (EA) in terms of $(EA)_0$ and time:

$$(EA) = (EA)_0 (1 - e^{-[(k_{+1}E_0 A_0 t)/(EA)_0]}) \tag{50}$$

If we then substitute Eq. (49) into Eq. (50),

$$(EA) = \frac{E_0 A_0}{K_m + A_0} [1 - e^{-k_{+1}t(K_m + A_0)}] \tag{51}$$

It can be seen that this function approaches the value of the first term [i.e., of the hypothetical steady state $(EA)_0$] when t is large. The exponential term is of importance only at low values of t, where it causes (EA) to diminish to zero at zero time. Thus Eq. (51) describes the time course of (EA) during the transient pre-steady-state phase of the reaction. The solid curve in Fig. 21 describes the actual time course of (EA). Also shown there are lines illustrating how the foregoing equations describe various portions of the curve at different times.

These relations provide a basis for analysis of data obtained by direct observation of an enzymic intermediate. It will ordinarily be more useful, however, to have a time course for product formation, as this is what can usually be followed experimentally. The differential expression for the transient phase is obtained by combining Eqs. (48) and (51):

$$\frac{dX}{dt} = \frac{k_{+2}E_0 A_0}{K_m + A_0} [1 - e^{-k_{+1}t(K_m + A_0)}] \tag{52}$$

This equation, too, can be integrated with $t = 0$, $X = 0$ describing the initial condition in the reaction mixture, to yield the time course of X, the product:

$$X = \frac{k_{+2}E_0 A_0 t}{K_m + A_0} - \frac{k_{+2}E_0 A_0}{(K_m + A_0)(k_{-1} + k_{+2} + k_{+1}A_0)} [1 - e^{-k_{+1}t(K_m + A_0)}] \tag{53}$$

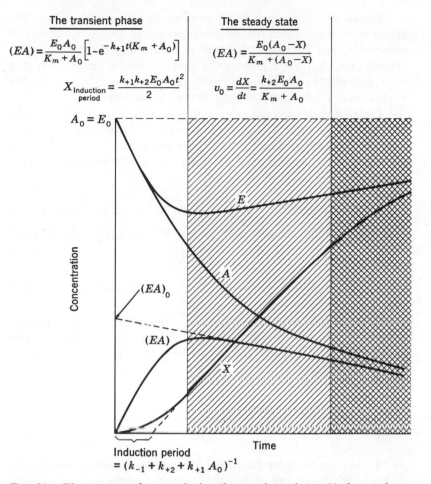

The transient phase

$$(EA) = \frac{E_0 A_0}{K_m + A_0}\left[1 - e^{-k_{+1}t(K_m + A_0)}\right]$$

$$X_{\substack{\text{Induction} \\ \text{period}}} = \frac{k_{+1}k_{+2}E_0 A_0 t^2}{2}$$

The steady state

$$(EA) = \frac{E_0(A_0 - X)}{K_m + (A_0 - X)}$$

$$v_0 = \frac{dX}{dt} = \frac{k_{+2}E_0 A_0}{K_m + A_0}$$

$A_0 = E_0$

E

A

$(EA)_0$

(EA)

X

Concentration

Time

Induction period
$= (k_{-1} + k_{+2} + k_{+1}A_0)^{-1}$

FIG. 21. Time course of events during the transient phase. X, the product; (EA), the enzyme-substrate complex (cf. case II, Fig. 4, Chapter 2).

Note that when t is large, a plot of X vs. t has a slope of

$$\frac{k_{+2}E_0 A_0}{K_m + A_0}$$

i.e., this is the steady-state rate, as expected. Extrapolation of this steady-state rate to $X = 0$ gives the relation

$$\frac{k_{+2}E_0 A_0 t}{K_m + A_0} = \frac{k_{+2}E_0 A_0}{(K_m + A_0)(k_{-1} + k_{+2} + k_{+1}A_0)}$$

from which

$$t_{X=0} = (k_{-1} + k_{+2} + k_{+1}A_0)^{-1} = [k_{+1}(K_m + A)]^{-1} \tag{54}$$

Figure 21 shows this result graphically. In practical use, this extrapolated time, called the induction period, is determined at several values of A_0 and Eq. (54) is then used to obtain separate values for k_{+1} and the sum $(k_{-1} + k_{+2})$. Since the value of k_{+2} is generally known from the steady-state determination of V, this procedure permits evaluation of all the rate constants in the mechanism.

Equation (53) also provides a further means for evaluating the constants. If measurements of X can be secured at such short times that the exponential term dominates the function [i.e., $k_{+1}t(k_m + A_0) \ll 1$], the equation can be simplified by expansion of the exponential. Disregarding all but the first two terms,

$$X = \frac{k_{+1}k_{+2}E_0A_0t^2}{2}$$

to a very good approximation. Since k_{+2} is known from V and since

$$K_m = \frac{k_{+2} + k_{-1}}{k_{+1}}$$

and is also generally known from steady-state measurements, again all the constants can be evaluated separately.

What we have seen here is that rational methods can be applied to the analysis of the transient phase, certainly for the one-substrate model system and for some additional systems considered by Laidler (3) and by Gutfreund (1). In some ways the theoretical analysis is simpler and more direct than steady-state analysis.

FLOW METHODS

Theoretical tools for evaluating rate constants from a combination of transient phase and steady-state measurements are not lacking. It remains to be considered how one can actually go about making measurements during the transient phase of an enzyme-catalyzed reaction. The time interval available for such measurements is very short, being not more than a small fraction of a second.[2] As a consequence, these procedures generally require rather elaborate equipment capable of (a) mixing substrate and enzyme solutions very rapidly without denaturing the enzyme, (b) responding instantaneously and quantitatively to very small changes in product concentration, and (c) making

---

[2] To observe enzyme-substrate complexes directly, it is necessary to have the enzyme and substrate present at comparable concentrations. The time available for observation then will be of the order $1/k_{+1}A$. For reactions that are diffusion-controlled, k_{+1} will be in the range 10^8 to 10^9 M^{-1} sec^{-1}.

a suitable record of those changes with time. Most of the equipment that has been designed to provide this combination of capabilities has, understandably, utilized spectrophotometric measurement, with oscilloscope recording of the photomultiplier signal.

The first equipment devised for measurements of reaction times in the milliseconds range was that of Hartridge and Roughton (4), which avoided the requirement that the detecting device must respond instantaneously, but at the expense of much reactant material. The instrumentation used involved rapid mixing followed by rapid continuous flow through a long tube. Observations made at different points along the tube then corresponded to different points in the reaction time. For studying enzyme-catalyzed reactions, a more generally useful procedure is that subsequently devised by Chance (5,6), commonly called the stopped-flow technique. This method has the advantage that reasonably small quantities of enzyme can be used, as no lengthy continuous flow is required, but does demand equipment having time constants smaller than those of the chemical system to be measured. As the procedure is most commonly used at present, the enzyme and substrate solutions are injected simultaneously from syringes into a mixing chamber, from which the mixture flows rapidly to an observation cell, where flow is halted abruptly and spectrophotometric observation begins. All of this can be accomplished with small volumes of solution in times of the order of 1 msec in favorable cases. The technology and lore of flow techniques have been reviewed in various aspects by Chance (7), Roughton (8), and Caldin (9). Flow methods are also discussed in some detail by Gutfreund (10).

It appears, then, that both the theoretical and engineering problems of rapid reaction techniques have largely been solved at the milliseconds level of resolution and it remains to be inquired what is demanded of the reaction system itself to make such studies feasible. If the analysis is to proceed by following the concentration of (EA) (Fig. 21), what is required is an (EA) with spectral (or fluorescence) properties very different from those of either E or A and, generally speaking, a large absorptivity coefficient. As might be expected, there are not many enzyme-catalyzed reactions that fulfill these conditions. The peroxidase and catalase-catalyzed reactions do, however, and the elegant work of Chance (7,11) with these enzymes depends on such considerations.

If, alternatively, the analysis is to proceed by following the concentration of product, it is the product that must have special spectral properties. With a number of the hydrolases, in particular those which have low specificity for some features of substrate structure, this has been easy to arrange. The synthesis of chromogenic substrates for several proteases and phosphatases, for example, has made stopped-flow analysis a very useful tool for those enzymes. It is also a fortunate circumstance that ionic reactions, especially protonations, are very rapid, certainly exceeding anything measurable by flow techniques. Consequently, indicator dyes may often be used in flow studies of reactions that involve release or uptake of protons. Moreover, the potential use of the technique has been broadened substantially by the introduction of what is called flow quenching. Here, the enzyme and substrate solutions are mixed as in all other flow techniques but the reaction mixture then flows into a second mixing chamber (rather than an observation cell), where it is mixed with a chemical quenching agent, often a strong acid, that very rapidly stops the reaction. With constant flow velocity, the reaction time permitted is simply a function of the tube length between mixing chambers. The quenched reaction mixture may then be analyzed for product concentration by any convenient method. This technique, which has been reviewed by Roughton (8), Caldin (9), and Gutfreund (10), should be useful for a large number of enzyme-catalyzed reactions unapproachable by other flow methods.

RELAXATION METHODS

Although the flow methods have permitted measurements on a milliseconds time scale, rather than the seconds scale accessible with conventional methods, a large number of important reactions still cannot be approached directly without yet faster techniques. Even the " slow " rate-determining steps at maximum velocity are often too rapid for measurement by flow methods. Moreover, although one may have considerable latitude in adjusting velocities by control of concentrations in the bimolecular steps, direct measurement of ionic reactions, for example, will not in general be possible by flow methods. To fill this gap in the chemical kinetics of fast reactions, Eigen and his associates developed the relaxation methods, which are capable of dealing with kinetic observations on a microseconds time scale. Bimolecular reactions with rate constants as high as $10^9 \ M^{-1}\text{sec}^{-1}$ can be dealt with by these powerful techniques. Moreover, a number of important applications of relaxation kinetics to enzyme-catalyzed reactions have been made, most notably by Hammes and his co-workers (12–17).

The general principles on which relaxation analysis is based are simple enough. A reaction at equilibrium or, if equilibrium is very far in one direction, in a steady state, is subjected to a change in an intensive variable (e.g., temperature or pressure) that affects the equilibrium. Adjustment of the reaction to the new equilibrium is then observed by spectrophotometric or other means.

In a typical experiment, an enzyme-catalyzed reaction is at equilibrium in a specially equipped spectrophotometer cell. A large electrical capacitor is discharged through the solution, raising the temperature 10 degrees within 1 msec (a "temperature jump") and observation begins.[3] Clearly, oscilloscope recording of the events during the "relaxation" to the new equilibrium position can start very soon indeed after those events begin. The great advantage of the method is that neither mixing nor transportation of the reaction system need be done to initiate the observation of changes. Thus the time-limiting features of the flow methods are avoided.

If the change in equilibrium position is substantial, the kinetic behavior will be complex, involving squared terms in some concentrations and some products of concentrations. If the change is very small, however, these complex terms are not significant and the change in concentration as a function of time during "relaxation" is simply proportional to the amount by which the concentration differs from the equilibrium concentration. That is, under these circumstances (very close to equilibrium) all changes are indistinguishable from simple first-order behavior.

The usual form in which the relationship is presented is the following:

$$\frac{d\,\Delta C}{dt} = -\frac{\Delta C}{\tau}$$

where ΔC is the tiny increment in concentration away from equilibrium and τ is a constant, called the relaxation time, characteristic of the reaction. Obviously τ is just the inverse pseudo-first-order rate constant for this process. It relates to actual rate constants and equilibrium concentrations in the reaction systems in ways that depend on the particular reactions involved.

For example, in the isolated formation of an enzyme-substrate complex, since the net velocity of the reaction must equal $k_{+1}AE - k_{-1}(EA)$ for any concentration of A, and the velocity for small increments away from equilibrium is defined in terms of τ as indicated above, $k_{-1} + k_{+1}(A_{eq} + E_{eq}) = \tau^{-1}$. Determination of τ for several values of $(A_{eq} + E_{eq})$ can then yield both rate constants.

In isomerization reactions of the type $(EA)_1 \rightleftharpoons (EA)_2$, a kind of reaction in enzyme mechanisms that steady-state kinetics generally fails to detect, τ^{-1} comes out to be equal to $(k_{+1} + k_{-1})$. Here again,

---

[3] It is necessary, of course, that the ΔH for the reaction be sufficient for this magnitude of "jump" to cause a significant shift in equilibrium. It is also essential to have a sufficiently sensitive detection system to monitor the concentration of at least one reactant with high accuracy.

if the equilibrium concentrations (and therefore k_{+1}/k_{-1}) are known, both the individual rate constants can be obtained. As reaction systems become more complex, however, including the sequential reactions of enzymic catalysis, the simple identification of each observed relaxation time with one of the steps would be erroneous. Although the discernible number of relaxation times must represent a minimum estimate of the number of elementary reaction steps in the sequence, the analysis for the rate constants is more complex than in the simple cases cited above. It is, nevertheless, a feasible procedure.

A further, and especially interesting, development of relaxation techniques involves the use of periodic perturbations rather than the "jump" or step function perturbation illustrated above. For this purpose, ultrasonic waves have been used to provide a periodic pressure perturbation. The system has the great convenience that it also provides a detection system independent of any special properties of the reactants. The following discussion will indicate how this procedure operates.

Although the fact is little used experimentally, it is true that the equilibrium positions of many reactions in aqueous solution are sensitive to pressure. Laidler has discussed the work done in this area (18). The heat of reaction consists of ΔE^0, the change in internal energy in the standard state and a $p \Delta V^0$ term, pressure times the increase in volume in the standard state. It is evident that reactions in which the reactants undergo major volume changes, either because of structural alterations or, especially, because of changes in the size of hydration shells, will respond to pressure changes. Thus, ionic reactions are expected to be particularly sensitive, as may also reactions resulting in conformational changes in proteins.

If, then, such a reaction at equilibrium is subjected to a pressure perturbation, its equilibrium position will shift, at a rate determined by the relaxation time for the system. Pressure jump experiments fully analogous to the temperature jump work can be done. If the perturbation is made periodic, the equilibrium will tend to oscillate between its states at the two extremes of pressure. At a characteristic frequency determined by the relaxation time, the reaction system will just be able to "keep up" in phase with the ultrasonic signal. At higher frequencies the oscillation will tend to disappear. One consequence of this is that less of the ultrasonic signal will be absorbed by the system at the higher frequencies. Thus τ can be determined by monitoring the transmission of the perturbing signal itself over a range of frequencies.[4]

[4] In the present state of technology, however, ultrasonic pressure relaxation experiments are difficult to do, both because of the complex equipment required and the rather large volumes of enzyme solution required.

As noted above, relaxation methods have been used in a number of investigations of enzyme-catalyzed reactions. Two generalizations from the results of this work are particularly striking. The first is that very many of the rate constants for the formation of enzyme-substrate complexes are near the theoretical maximum (10^8 to 10^9 $M^{-1}sec^{-1}$ for molecules of the sizes involved here). The large differences in equilibrium constants for complex formation are therefore accountable to variations in the rate constant for the dissociation reaction. The second is that it is surprising how many elementary steps appear in an enzyme-catalyzed reaction. It seems that it is very common for complexes to isomerize, i.e., to undergo some rearrangement, prior to further reaction. This is a matter of very substantial importance. If such conformation changes are in fact a general accompaniment of the individual steps in enzyme mechanisms and if they often become rate-limiting, the inference of detailed catalytic mechanisms from kinetic data will be severely hampered. The forms of the equations are still valid in this case but the effort to account for specific rate constants in terms of electronic displacements, etc., will have to take into account the fact that evaluated rate constants are all only minimum estimates.

Further developments in the application of the elegant relaxation methods to enzyme-catalyzed reactions are certain to be watched with great interest. Already the combination of stopped-flow and temperature jump relaxation methodology has yielded important new information about the ribonuclease mechanism (16,17), resulting in the proposal of an extremely detailed formal mechanism for the action of this enzyme (17). The combination technique is useful wherever the equilibrium position of the overall reaction studied is such that the overwhelmingly predominant enzyme complex at equilibrium is with one reactant. To study complexes with other reactants in this reaction, the enzyme and the desired reactant are mixed in a rapid flow, which is then stopped in a temperature jump cell. The relaxation measurements are then made before the reaction can proceed to such an extent that interfering amounts of the tightly bound product accumulate.

GENERAL REFERENCES

Laidler, K. J.: *The Chemical Kinetics of Enzyme Action*, Oxford, London, 1958.

Amdur, I., and G. G. Hammes: *Chemical Kinetics: Principles and Selected Topics*, McGraw-Hill, New York, 1966.

Gutfreund, H.: *An Introduction to the Study of Enzymes*, Wiley, New York, 1965.

Eigen, M., and G. G. Hammes: *Advan. Enzymol.*, **25**: (1963).
Bernhard, S. A., *The Structure and Function of Enzymes*, Benjamin, New York, 1968.

SPECIFIC REFERENCES

1. Gutfreund, H.: *Discussions Faraday Soc.*, **20**: 167 (1955).
2. Morales, M. F., and D. E. Goldman: *J. Am. Chem. Soc.*, **77**: 6069 (1955).
3. Laidler, K. J.: *Canad. J. Chem.*, **33**: 1614 (1955).
4. Hartridge, H., and F. J. R. Roughton: *Proc. Roy. Soc.* (*London*), *Ser. A*, **104**: 376 (1923).
5. Chance, B.: *J. Franklin Inst.*, **229**: 455 (1940).
6. Chance, B.: *Discussions Faraday Soc.*, **17**: 120 (1954).
7. Chance, B.: in S. L. Friess, E. S. Lewis, and A. Weissberger (eds.), *Technique of Organic Chemistry*, Vol. VIII: *Investigation of Rates and Mechanisms of Reactions*, Interscience, New York, 1963.
8. Roughton, F. J. R.: in S. L. Friess, E. S. Lewis, and A. Weissberger (eds.), *Technique of Organic Chemistry*, Vol. VIII: *Investigation of Rates and Mechanisms of Reactions*, Interscience, New York, 1963.
9. Caldin, E. F.: *Fast Reactions in Solution*, Wiley, New York, 1964.
10. Gutfreund, H.: *An Introduction to the Study of Enzymes*, Wiley, New York, 1965, pp. 120–133.
11. Chance, B.: *Advan. Enzymol.*, **12**: 153 (1951).
12. Hammes, G. G.: *Science*, **151**: 1507 (1966).
13. Cathou, R. E., and G. G. Hammes: *J. Am. Chem. Soc.*, **86**: 3240 (1964).
14. French, T. C., and G. G. Hammes: *J. Am. Chem. Soc.*, **87**: 4669 (1965).
15. Cathou, R. E., and G. G. Hammes: *J. Am. Chem. Soc.*, **87**: 4674 (1965).
16. Erman, J. E., and G. G. Hammes: *J. Am. Chem. Soc.*, **88**: 5607 (1966).
17. Erman, J. E., and G. G. Hammes: *J. Am. Chem. Soc.*, **88**: 5614 (1966).
18. Laidler, K. J.: *The Chemical Kinetics of Enzyme Action*, Oxford, London, 1958, pp. 210–226.

12

THE DIRECTION
OF ELECTRONIC DISPLACEMENT—
ANALOGUE SUBSTRATES

Presuming that the methods outlined in Part II have yielded the
formal mechanism for an enzyme-catalyzed reaction, the methods given
in Chaps. 10 and 11 should permit distinguishing the numbers and kinds
of kinetically significant intermediates. The most important result of
all this can be the evaluation of some individual rate and equilibrium
constants under some conditions. The task then remaining is to utilize
such data to show what chemical features of the enzyme are required
in the various individual steps in the overall catalyzed reaction. One
of the most general questions that can be directed to this point experimentally concerns the qualitative direction in which the enzyme dis-
places the electron distribution in the substrate.

THE PRINCIPLE

The business of enzymes, whether viewed teleologically as synthetic
or degradative in function, is clearly the making and breaking of bonds,
i.e., of electronic alteration of substrates. This should not be taken to
imply that the mechanism is always predominantly electronic at all
steps, but the result surely has electronic character and a detailed
description of any catalyzed reaction must include the direction of
electronic displacement. The most fruitful direct approach to this
question is through the use of analogue substrates.[1]

The principle involved in this work is simple. In essence, one tries
to build into the substrate an electronic displacement that partially

---

[1] It will be noted that this is a further usage of analogue substrates, distinct in
principle from those presented in earlier chapters.

mimics what the enzyme does. If such alteration systematically facilitates the catalysis, it is reasonable to conclude that the electronic displacement caused by the enzyme is in the same direction. For example, suppose that in splitting the substrate AB, an enzyme is presumed to displace the electronic field away from A toward B. It should be possible to test this hypothesis by determining the variation of the particular rate constant for AB splitting in a series of A'B substrates, where A' may be any of many residues of different electronegativity. If the specificity of the enzyme prevents varying A, variations of B may be used to achieve the same result. It is of course essential to know the circumstances for securing the individual rate constant for the bond scission step. This method should be of very general applicability. It seems likely to fail systematically *only* if the rate-limiting process at maximum velocity is a conformational change in the enzyme or a dissociation of product rather than an electronic event involving the substrate.

The systematic exploitation of this general approach has not been very popular in enzymology, probably because a number of earlier studies proved difficult to interpret. The difficulties did not arise from any ambiguity concerning the electronic nature of substituents; Ingold's early treatment of inductive effects (1) was certainly adequate for the necessary qualitative considerations. For that matter, the semiquantitative empirical Hammett treatment (2,3) or the similarly based Taft equation (4) provides a suitable basis for such work. What was lacking was an adequate basis of enzyme kinetic theory. The formal mechanisms had not been elucidated and the investigators had no way of knowing what rate constant or combination of constants was being affected. Pseudo-one-substrate kinetics were assumed, sometimes with the further assumption that equilibrium conditions obtained; true initial velocities were rarely assured. Interpretation was of course somewhat tenuous under these circumstances. Nevertheless, these are fascinating studies, and modern reinterpretation often shows them to have been fundamentally sound. The following few examples may suffice to illustrate the point.

APPLICATIONS

In 1953 Ormerod (5) studied the cholinesterase-catalyzed hydrolysis of various substituted benzoyl cholines. The maximum velocity of hydrolysis was found to correlate well with the Hammett σ constant for the ring substituent (i.e., with the electron withdrawing power of the substituent).[2] The conclusion was that lowering the electron density on the ester carbon facilitated the cleavage, and on this basis Ormerod postulated an electrophilic displacement by the enzyme at the carbonyl oxygen to facilitate a nucleophilic attack on the carbon atom. This work was done under naive assumptions (notably, that the maximum velocity was controlled solely by a reaction cleaving the C—O ester bond), but it is easy to place the phenomenon in subsequent, more detailed mechanisms for cholinesterase (6). I. B. Wilson has made very nice use of these same principles applied to inhibitors rather than substrates in implicating an electrophilic component in the catalysis by acetyl-cholinesterase and other hydrolases (6,7).

Nath and Rydon also studied the correlation of both V and K_m for β-glucosidase with the Hammett σ for substituents in a series of sub-stituted phenyl-β-D-glucosides (8). Here, too, although the work was done with a crude enzyme preparation and kinetic assumptions naive by present standards, the correlations obtained very probably did reflect an electrophilic displacement by an enzyme group facilitating a nucleo-philic attack. As in the case of cholinesterase, however, the nucleophile involved in attack on the substrate is also an enzymic group rather than a form of hydroxide ion, as was then presumed. Both of these enzymes are now known to proceed by double-displacement mechanisms (i.e., they involve substituted enzyme intermediates). Somewhat similar studies were carried out in this period by Gawron et al. (9) on a lipase and by Dodgson et al. (10) on arylsulfatase, securing clear correlations of kinetic coefficients with Hammett constants. Although not done with simple equilibrium assumptions, these studies, too, suffered from lack of definition at the level of two-substrate formal analysis.

Today, however, the enzymologist does not labor under such handicaps and there is no reason why determining the direction of electronic displacement should not be a standard method. Some success-ful applications of this approach have in fact been made. Physical organic chemists have naturally been interested in effects of this kind and various substrates have been used in this connection with chymo-trypsin. The excellent review by Bender and Kézdy (11) summarizes this work. The principal study to be mentioned in the present context is that

---

[2] The Hammett equation is $\log(k/k_0) = \sigma\rho$, where k and k_0 are the rate constants for the reaction with a ring-substituted phenyl compound and the unsubstituted parent compound, respectively. Substituents are characterized by σ values, which indicate their electron-withdrawing power. Different reactions have different ρ values, depending on their sensitivities to electron supply at the reaction site, a positive value indicating that the velocity is increased by electron withdrawal. A positive ρ therefore indicates that the attack on the substituted molecule is by a nucleophilic reagent.

of Caplow and Jencks (12) who showed that the deacylation step in the chymotrypsin mechanism (i.e., hydrolysis of the acyl-chymotrypsin-substituted enzyme intermediate) has a Hammett ρ constant of $+2.1$. This result clearly indicates attack by a nucleophile, in this case one derived from the solvent water. Most of the enzymes investigated via the systematic formal approach subscribed to in this book, however, have not been studied from this point of view.

One exception is rhodanese, whose formal mechanism was dealt with in Chap. 9. Use of substrate analogues for thiosulfate had yielded the result that the rate of rupture of the sulfur-sulfur bond of thiosulfate limited the overall maximum velocity of the enzyme-catalyzed thiosulfate-cyanide reaction. The same data considered from the point of view of electronic displacement indicated that displacement away from the transferable sulfur atom, toward the inner sulfur atom, facilitated the bond cleavage by the enzyme (13).

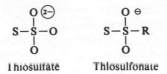

Thiosulfate   Thiosulfonate

Thus all of the organic thiosulfonates tested were much more easily split at maximum velocities than was inorganic thiosulfate, although the thiosulfonates were no better bound to the enzyme than was thiosulfate. Since it is clear kinetically that the maximum velocity for thiosulfate was dominated by the rate constant for the S—S bond scission, this result led to the conclusion that, electronically, the thiosulfonates were nearer the transition state situation than was thiosulfate. Accordingly, since any of the organic residues used as substituent is an electron sink relative to the —O$^-$ it replaced, the conclusion followed that electron withdrawal from the transferable sulfur atom, toward the central sulfur atom of thiosulfate, facilitated the action of the enzyme in cleaving the S—S bond. The observed kinetic behavior was qualitatively like that obtained in the uncatalyzed reaction of thiosulfate and thiosulfonates with the nucleophile CN$^-$ (Hammett $\rho = +0.5$).

From this evidence it is a reasonable inference that rhodanese cleaves thiosulfate by apposition of an electrophilic group to the oxygen atoms of the substrate, with a resultant electronic shift to a distribution qualitatively similar to that in the thiosulfonates. This is followed by transfer of the outer sulfur atom to a nucleophilic residue in the enzyme and discharge of sulfite ion, leaving the sulfur-substituted enzyme intermediate.

It should be clear from the foregoing example that information concerning the direction of electronic displacement can be extremely valuable to the investigator in designing further studies. The rhodanese mechanism at this level of resolution clearly requires an electrophilic group that will combine with the oxygen rather than the sulfur of thiosulfate and, further, an enzymic sulfur nucleophile in close spatial juxtaposition. This information has guided the search for, and subsequent interpretation of, evidence regarding specific residues in the active center of the enzyme. Direct efforts to identify the residues fulfilling these functions in the catalyzed reaction have resulted in the implication of a bound zinc ion (14) and an essential enzymic sulfhydryl group (15) as the probable electrophile and nucleophile, respectively, in this mechanism. It is emphasized, however, that little of this advantage could have accrued if the formal mechanism and the circumstances for isolating the relevant rate constant had not been known.

GENERAL REFERENCES

Jencks, W. P.: *Ann. Rev. Biochem.*, **32**: (1963).
Bender, M. L., and F. J. Kézdy: *Ann. Rev. Biochem.*, **34**: (1965).
Westheimer, F. H.: *Advan. Enzymol.*, **24**: (1962).

SPECIFIC REFERENCES

1. Ingold, C. K.: *Structure and Mechanism in Organic Chemistry*, Cornell University Press, Ithaca, 1953.
2. Hammett, L. P.: *Physical-Organic Chemistry*, McGraw-Hill, New York, 1940.
3. Jaffé, H. H.: *Chem. Rev.*, **53**: 191 (1953).
4. Taft, R. W., Jr.: *Steric Effects in Organic Chemistry*, **1**: 556 (1956).
5. Ormerod, W. E.: *Biochem. J.*, **54**: 701 (1953).
6. Wilson, I. B.: in P. D. Boyer, H. Lardy, and K. Myrbäck (eds.), *The Enzymes*, 2nd ed., Vol. 4, Academic, New York, 1960, p. 501.
7. Metzger, H. P., and I. B. Wilson: *Biochemistry*, **3**: 926 (1964).
8. Nath, R. L., and H. N. Rydon: *Biochem. J.*, **57**: 1 (1954).
9. Gawron, O., C. J. Grelecki, and M. Duggan: *Arch. Biochem. Biophys.*, **44**: 455 (1953).
10. Dodgson, K. S., B. Spencer, and K. Williams: *Biochem. J.*, **64**: 216 (1956).
11. Bender, M. L., and F. J. Kézdy: *Ann. Rev. Biochem.*, **34**: 49 (1965).
12. Caplow, M., and W. P. Jencks: *Biochemistry*, **1**: 883 (1962).
13. Mintel, R., and J. Westley: *J. Biol. Chem.*, **241**: 3381 (1966).
14. Volini, M., F. DeToma, and J. Westley: *J. Biol. Chem.*, **242**: 5220 (1967).
15. Wang, S.-F., and M. Volini: *J. Biol. Chem.*, **243**: 5465 (1968).

13

THERMODYNAMIC AND ACTIVATION PARAMETERS: VARIATION OF TEMPERATURE, DIELECTRIC CONSTANT, IONIC STRENGTH

It is commonplace that the velocities of chemical reactions increase sharply with temperature. It is also well known that catalysts provide reaction pathways having lower free energies of activation. That is, the velocities of catalyzed reactions are somewhat less affected by temperature than are those of the corresponding uncatalyzed reactions. The variation of enzyme-catalyzed reaction velocity with temperature, however, is likely to be a complex phenomenon. For one thing, the deleterious effects of temperature on the catalyst itself must be taken into account. Moreover, the several different steps in any enzyme mechanism are virtually certain to have quantitatively different responses to temperature. Perhaps it is little wonder that earlier enzymologists reported simple "temperature optima" for enzymes under specified conditions, without the implication (or the hope) that such information could be useful analytically. The considerable utility of thermodynamic and activation parameters in organic mechanism work, however, and the opportunity to isolate individual reactions in enzymic catalysis kinetically have combined to suggest that this was too pessimistic a view.

For example, whenever it can be shown that a Michaelis constant approximates a true equilibrium constant over a reasonable temperature range, or whenever you can determine an equilibrium constant in a mechanism directly, the opportunity arises to look for a conformational change in either the enzyme (an "induced fit") or the substrate ("freezing") that may be a necessary accompaniment to binding, since such a change must appear as a nonelectrostatic contribution to the entropy term for binding. Similarly, when a single rate constant dominates the maximum velocity term over a reasonable temperature range, one has the opportunity to find out the extent to which electronic factors are

144

involved in the catalysis, as these must appear in the enthalpy of activation.[1]

This chapter explores some ways in which such evidence may be obtained and related to the roles of different kinds of enzymic groups in a mechanism, especially to: (a) the forces involved in attachment of a substrate to an enzyme, (b) those aspects of a particular catalysis which are attributable to bond weakening or to "altered opportunity," and (c) how strong an enzymic nucleophile or electrophile must be to account for the observed rates. Determining the variation of rate and equilibrium constants with temperature, dielectric constant and ionic strength is the principal experimental tool in such study.

REVIEW OF FUNDAMENTAL THEORY

It will be useful at this point to recall some essentials of physical chemistry. The necessary thermodynamic relationships are direct and familiar. Equilibrium constants relate to standard free-energy changes: $\Delta G^0 = -RT \ln K$. Free-energy change is composed of changes in enthalpy and entropy: $\Delta G^0 = \Delta H^0 - T\Delta S^0$. The enthalpy term can be evaluated separately by determining the variation of equilibrium constant with temperature, according to the van't Hoff relationship

$$\frac{d \ln K}{dT} = \frac{\Delta H^0}{RT^2} \quad \text{or} \quad \ln K = \frac{\Delta H^0}{R} \times \frac{1}{T} + \text{a constant}$$

The entropy term can be resolved into electrostatic (ΔS_{es}) and non-electrostatic (ΔS_{nes}) contributions. The former contribution, generally attributed to release of solvent molecules attendant upon charge neutralization, or the opposite effect attendant upon augmentation of charge, can be determined from variation of the equilibrium constant with either dielectric constant or ionic strength according to a theory developed by Scatchard (2) and by Laidler (3). The nonelectrostatic entropy contribution can then be obtained by difference.

The slope of the plot $\ln K$ against inverse dielectric constant is $-Z_A Z_B e^2 / \mathbf{K} Tr$, where Z_A and Z_B are the valences of the interacting ionic charges, e is the electron charge, $\mathbf{K}$ is the Boltzmann constant and r is the radius of approach of the charge centers in the combined form.[2] In aqueous solution, ΔS_{es} in entropy units is approximately equal to

---

[1] Even granting that this is a somewhat simplistic point of view, since "strain" can appear in both enthalpy and nonelectrostatic entropy terms (1), the information to be obtained is interesting and can provide important clues to mechanism.

[2] For example, this form is the enzyme-substrate complex where the constant studied is the association constant for complex formation (K_s^{-1}).

1.1×10^{-4} times the slope of this plot. Further, either $Z_A Z_B$ or r can then be obtained if the other can be estimated indpendently. For example, ΔS_{es} is approximately equal to $-10 \, Z_A Z_B$ where r is 2 Å. Similarly, from Debye–Hückel theory, the slope of a plot of $\log K$ against the square root of ionic strength is approximately equal to $Z_A Z_B$ for dilute aqueous solutions at room temperature.

Application of these relationships to enzyme-catalyzed reactions is not entirely rigorous, as we shall see in the examples that follow. For one thing, there is the inadequate assumption that the addition of organic solvents (usually methanol) alters the dielectric constant of the reaction site in the enzyme to the same extent as that of the bulk medium. In addition, the relationships assume that it is possible to secure velocity values either extrapolated to zero ionic strength or at least evaluated at ionic strengths where the Debye–Hückel theory holds. Yet it is precisely in the most interesting cases, where the substrates are ionic, that this is especially difficult to do. Nevertheless, where results from the two experimental approaches (variation of ionic strength *and* dielectric constant) coincide, the semiquantitative conclusions that can be reached may yield important mechanistic information. The relatively ready accessibility of individual equilibrium constants by modern enzyme kinetic analysis should permit increased use of such data, especially in determining the degree of ionic involvement in substrate binding. Some examples will be given in later sections of this chapter.

Entirely analogous relationships are obtained for individual unimolecular rate constants in enzyme-catalyzed reactions. The free energy of activation $\Delta G^{\ddagger}$ is evaluated from the relationship

$$\Delta G^{\ddagger} = \ln \frac{\mathbf{K} T}{h} - \ln k$$

where $\mathbf{K}$ is the Boltzmann constant, h is Planck's constant, and T is the absolute temperature. The free energy of activation, like any other free energy, is made up of enthalpy and entropy terms

$$\Delta G^{\ddagger} = \Delta H^{\ddagger} - T \Delta S^{\ddagger}$$

The enthalpy of activation is closely related to the Arrhenius activation energy $\mathbf{E}$

$$\Delta H^{\ddagger} = \mathbf{E} - RT$$

The Arrhenius activation energy can be determined readily from the negative slope of the plot of the logarithm of the rate constant against the inverse absolute temperature

$$\ln k = -\frac{\mathbf{E}}{R} \times \frac{1}{T} + \text{a constant}$$

The entropy of activation has electrostatic and nonelectrostatic contributions. These are determined much as the contributions to entropy in an equilibrium, the only difference being that r^{-1} now must be replaced by the difference in inverse distances between the initial state considered and the transition state of the reaction. For example, for the sequence $A + B \overset{K_1}{\rightleftharpoons} (AB) \overset{k_{+2}}{\longrightarrow} C$, the entropy relationships stated above apply to the equilibrium K_1, where r equals r_{AB}, the distance between the charge centers of A and B in the complex. The same relationships can be stated for the rate constant k_{+2} except that r_{AB}^{-1} now is replaced by $(r_{AB\ddagger}^{-1} - r_{AB}^{-1})$, where the $r_{AB\ddagger}$ term refers to the charge separation in the transition state between (AB) and C. The application of the relationships to unimolecular steps, i.e., commonly to the steps that become rate determining at maximum velocities, can yield information about the nature of the key events that limit the extent of catalysis attained. From such information it is sometimes possible to come to rather broad conclusions about the nature of the catalysis as well as to secure indications regarding the specific enzymic groups involved.

Despite the very real advantages of this approach, however, stress must be placed on necessary precautions. Protein surfaces are *not* continuous dielectrically, behaving as the bulk solvent; salt effects *may* be primary kinetic effects but they *may also* be specific ion effects or secondary salt effects (on pK values of enzymic groups for example), or ion pairing effects (4). And, always, the calculations are not worthwhile unless adequate kinetic control is assured so that individual constants may be obtained. The "take-home lesson" here is twofold: (a) No shortcuts are allowed. It is essential to *establish* that the salt effects seen are primary kinetic effects, by eliminating the other categories of explanation experimentally; it is imperative to do complete kinetic experiments under each condition to obtain extrapolated values of kinetic coefficients, etc. (b) Even at its experimental best, this kind of experiment must not be overextended in its interpretation, as the assumptions made in the theoretical development are only very approximately correct.

SOME APPLICATIONS

Substantial thermodynamic and activation data have been obtained for several enzymes, including fumarase (5), chymotrypsin (6,7), and various other hydrolases (8–13). In the case of chymotrypsin, Bender and Kézdy (16) have shown that the rate constants for the individual steps in the hydrolysis of tryptophan esters by this enzyme are consistent with the overall equilibrium constant, i.e., that a complete energy profile may be drawn. Much of the earlier work has been well reviewed and discussed by Laidler (14) and by Lumry (15). Here we shall use two recent studies as illustrations.

Ribonuclease. In the course of relaxation kinetic studies on ribonuclease, Cathou and Hammes (17) determined the temperature dependence of the bimolecular and unimolecular events related to the binding of cytidine-3′-phosphate to the enzyme. The bimolecular process, which is the complexing reaction as such, has a very large rate constant, approaching the value expected for simple diffusion control of reaction velocity.[3] However, the enthalpy of activation is 13–19 kcal/mole and thus is larger than is ordinarily shown by purely diffusion-controlled reactions. Furthermore, the entropy of activation is 24–45 e.u. and this is well beyond what might be expected on electrostatic grounds (ca. 10 e.u. for interaction of univalent anion and cation) plus the "unmixing" nonelectrostatic contribution (ca. −8 e.u.). The only circumstance in simple accord with this analysis would be that in which only the dianionic form of the substrate could bind. Alternatively, these investigators suggest, the large positive entropy change might reflect a loosening of the enzyme structure accompanying binding. By such means, the rather large enthalpy of activation required in formation of the complex might be compensated in part by the entropy increase in the enzyme (19), with the net result of a favorable $\Delta G^{\ddagger}$ despite the large enthalpy term.

The unimolecular event that occurs on association of cytidine-3′-phosphate with the enzyme is an isomerization of the complex. Cathou and Hammes propose that this may be the formation of an inactive "misoriented" form of the complex, in which a phosphate hydroxyl group resides on the position normally taken by a sugar hydroxyl group in the active complex. The activation parameters evaluated for the process are in reasonable accord with this suggestion.

Rhodanese. A further example of this kind of study relates to the rhodanese mechanism discussed from other points of view in earlier chapters. There were three questions approachable by the techniques outlined above: (a) Did the binding process for the substrate thiosulfate involve substantial electrostatic forces? That is, was the binding group catonic and if so, what was its charge? (b) Was there a conformational change in the enzyme on binding substrate? (c) Was it necessary to propose the participation of a strong enzymic nucleophile in the bond

---

[3] Diffusion-controlled reactions are those in which essentially every molecular collision results in reaction (18). Such reactions characteristically have very small enthalpies of activation.

cleavage step that limits the maximum velocity of the rhodanese-catalyzed thiosulfate-cyanide reaction? That is, could the millionfold factor between the second-order rate constant for the spontaneous reaction and the first-order rate constant for thiosulfate S—S bond cleavage in the catalyzed reaction be explained entirely on the basis of the obvious gains in entropy factors in the enzymic mechanism and the electrophilic displacement discussed in Chap. 12? If so, attack by even a very weak enzymic nucleophile might be sufficient to cleave the S—S bond of the substrate; if not, it would be necessary to presume attack by a strong enzymic nucleophile. We shall examine these questions in turn.

1. It will be recalled that the rhodanese K_m for thiosulfate was shown to be a K_s and that even a hundredfold increase in k_{+2} would not make it a significant term in K_m. This fact permitted examination of the behavior of the enzyme-substrate complex formation as a function of ionic strength and of dielectric constant (20).[4] Various salts and solvents were tested in an effort to avoid specific effects. The questions of ion pairing and secondary effects were dealt with.

Qualitatively the results showed that increase of either ionic strength or dielectric constant interfered with thiosulfate binding. A plot of $\ln(K_s^{-1})$ against D^{-1} yielded an electrostatic contribution of $+16$ entropy units. A plot of $\log(K_s^{-1})$ against the square root of ionic strength yielded a slope of -2. These data strongly suggested a major ionic component in thiosulfate binding. $Z_A Z_B$ for a singly charged catonic site for thiosulfate would be -2, and at 2 Å approach, this would give an electrostatic entropy contribution of about $+20$ units. Furthermore, since inability to work at zero ionic strength and inability to alter the dielectric constant of the enzyme surface as much as that of the medium would have minimizing effects, and since 2 Å may well be too close an approach to presume for the charge center of anything as large as the thiosulfate anion, a true $Z_A Z_B$ of -4 might well be indicated. The inference drawn was that there must be a neutralization of charge on formation of the enzyme-thiosulfate complex. This bespeaks a cationic binding site for thiosulfate.

A later study (21) repeated some of the ΔS_{es} measurements and compared them with like studies of the spontaneous reaction under similar conditions. The deviations from ideality in the latter system were substantial, as expected, and the inference of a bivalent cationic binding site in the enzyme was accordingly strengthened. These

---

[4] As a matter of fact, since the unimolecular step in the mechanism turned out to be insensitive to these factors, the effects seen could have been related to the binding step even if equilibrium conditions had not prevailed.

TABLE 6.   *Thermodynamic Values for Dissociation of the* $(Rhodanese\text{-}SSO_3^{2-})$
Complex

$\Delta G^0_{300°}$ kcal/mole	$\Delta H^0_{300°}$ kcal/mole	$\Delta S^0_{300°}$ e.u.	$\Delta S^0_{es\,300°}$ e.u.	$\Delta S^0_{nes\,300°}$ e.u.
1.2 ± 1[a]	11 ± 1	33 ± 3	-22 ± 1	55 ± 4

[a] Values are given with their standard errors.
Adapted from Tables V–VII of K. Leininger and J. Westley, *J. Biol. Chem.*, **243**: 1892 (1968). Used by permission.

considerations led to a successful search for a divalent metal ion in the active center, where it presumably serves both as a cationic binding site and as the electrophilic group active in the subsequent bond cleavage step (22).

2. The availability of K_s for thiosulfate also made possible a kinetic approach to the question of conformational change on substrate binding. This was of interest primarily because of the possibility of unambiguous interpretation. As pointed out by Laidler (23) some time ago, nonelectrostatic entropy contributions of too large a magnitude to be accountable to "unmixing" or other obvious mechanistic factors probably indicate conformational changes. Bender and Kézdy have indicated that restricted rotation ("freezing") in substrates could also give rise to such effects, but the present example, with SSO_3^{2-} ion as the substrate, seems to eliminate the latter possibility from consideration. $K_s^{SSO_3^{2-}}$ was determined (21) with the use of Cleland's statistical procedures (24) for a variety of temperatures and in media of various dielectric constants. The calculated values for the thermodynamic parameters are given in Table 6 with their standard errors. A very large nonelectrostatic entropy term is associated with thiosulfate binding, probably indicating a major conformation change in the enzyme.

Fluorescence polarization studies of the enzyme that have subsequently been completed (25) seem in accord with the above inference. It should be noted, however, that the indicated change of conformation may well not be an essential part of the catalytic mechanism at all but simply the response of a rather mobile structure to a major change in environment. The change is in the "tightening" rather than the "loosening" direction that might be expected in accordance with Hammes' idea (19) of "entropy compensation" that proposes a catalytic role for conformation changes. Perhaps it would be astonishing if there were no conformational change in response to bringing a divalent anion into a hydrophobic site in the protein.

TABLE 7. *Values of the Activation Parameters for Cleavage of the S—S Bond of Thiosulfate by Rhodanese, and Estimated Contributions to the Catalysis*

Parameter	Uncatalyzed Reaction with CN^-	Reaction with Rhodanese	Contribution to Catalysis	Possible Mechanism
$\Delta S_{es}^{\ddagger}$	-9 e.u.	0 e.u.	$2\frac{1}{2}$ kcal/mole	Elimination of anion-anion interaction
$\Delta S_{nes}^{\ddagger}$	-29 e.u.	-25 e.u.	1 kcal/mole	Elimination of un-mixing and SSO_3^{2-} orientation factors, partially counter-balanced by new constraints including possible conformation change on attack by enzymic nucleophile
$\Delta H^{\ddagger}$	12 kcal/mole	7 kcal/mole	5 kcal/mole	Weakening of S—S bond by electrophilic displacement and concerted attack by strong enzymic nucleophile
$\Delta G^{\ddagger}$	$23\frac{1}{2}$ kcal/mole	15 kcal/mole	$8\frac{1}{2}$ kcal/mole	

Adapted from Tables V–VII of K. Leininger and J. Westley, *J. Biol. Chem.*, **243**: 1892 (1968). Used by permission.

3. The question relating to possible participation of a strong enzymic nucleophile in cleaving the S—S bond of thiosulfate was approachable since the rate constant for this step was known to be the limiting factor in the maximum velocity. The question arose because of the evidently very large entropic advantage which the enzyme-catalyzed reaction has over the spontaneous thiosulfate-cyanide reaction. The double-displacement mode of catalysis has great inherent power for reactions between two like-charge ions, as this form affords the opportunity to dissipate the ionic charge of the first substrate by discharging a product before the second substrate is required to approach. For the thiosulfate-cyanide reaction, this electrostatic entropy factor alone could account for a difference in free energies of activation as large as 6 kcal/mole. Moreover, the change from bimolecularity to unimolecularity in the rate-limiting step would diminish the $\Delta G^{\ddagger}$ by

from 1.4 to 2.4 kcal/mole, as a nonelectrostatic entropy contribution, depending on whether the 10 M assumption (Chap. 6) or the "unmixing" factor of 8 e.u. is used. An additional small contribution based on the likelihood that the thiosulfate ion is firmly oriented in the complex would bring the total ideal entropic advantage to a figure very near the total change in $\Delta G^{\ddagger}$ to be accounted for. If all this entropic advantage could be realized, either very little electrophilic displacement would be required to achieve bond cleavage by an enzymic nucleophile as strong as cyanide or, alternatively, with a major electrophilic displacement such as an enzymic metal ion might provide, attack by a very weak nucleophile might serve.

The study was carried out simultaneously with the thermodynamic study of $K_s^{SSO_3^{2-}}$ mentioned above (21) and the activation parameters for thiosulfate S—S bond cleavage by the enzyme were obtained (Table 7). From these results it is clear that the theoretical entropic advantage could not all be realized in practice, largely, it appears, because of the necessity for working at rather substantial ionic strengths. There may also be a further "tightening" conformational change or other additional constraint in this reaction as well. A major change in enthalpy of activation is required. It thus appeared that even with a considerable electrophilic displacement, an enzymic nucleophile not markedly weaker than cyanide would be required in the bond cleavage mechanism. Firm evidence for participation of an enzymic sulfhydryl group in the mechanism (26), earlier suspected on various grounds (27), probably relates to this finding.

GENERAL REFERENCES

Laidler, K. J.: *The Chemical Kinetics of Enzyme Action*, Oxford, London, 1958.

Lumry, R.: in P. D. Boyer, H. Lardy, and K. Myrbäck (eds.), *The Enzymes*, 2nd ed., Vol. 1, Academic, New York, 1959.

Amis, E. S.: *Solvent Effects on Reaction Rates*, Academic, New York, 1966.

SPECIFIC REFERENCES

1. Jencks, W. P.: in N. O. Kaplan and E. P. Kennedy (eds.), *Current Aspects of Biochemical Energetics*, Academic, New York, 1966, p. 273.
2. Scatchard, G.: *Chem. Rev.*, **10**: 229 (1932).
3. Laidler, K. J.: *Reaction Kinetics*, Vol. II, Pergamon Press, Oxford, 1963.
4. Davies, C. W.: *Progr. Reaction Kinetics*, **1**: 161 (1961).

5. Brant, D. A., L. B. Barnett, and R. A. Alberty: *J. Am. Chem. Soc.*, **79**: 1526 (1957).
6. Snoke, J. E., and H. Neurath: *J. Biol. Chem.*, **182**: 577 (1950).
7. Barnard, M. L., and K. J. Laidler: *J. Am. Chem. Soc.*, **74**: 6099 (1952).
8. Laidler, K. J., and M. C. Ethier: *Arch. Biochem. Biophys.*, **44**: 338 (1953).
9. Lumry, R., E. L. Smith, and R. R. Glantz: *J. Am. Chem. Soc.*, **73**: 4330 (1951).
10. Casey, E. J., and K. J. Laidler: *J. Am. Chem. Soc.*, **72**: 2159 (1950).
11. Wall, M. C., and K. J. Laidler: *Arch. Biochem. Biophys.*, **43**: 299 (1953).
12. Bernhard, S. A.: *J. Am. Chem. Soc.*, **77**: 1966 (1955).
13. Wilson, I. B., and E. Cabib: *J. Am. Chem. Soc.*, **78**: 202 (1956).
14. Laidler, K. J.: *The Chemical Kinetics of Enzyme Action*, Oxford, London, 1958, Chapter 7.
15. Lumry, R.: in P. D. Boyer, M. Lardy, and K. Myrbäck (eds.), *The Enzymes*, 2nd ed., Vol. 1, Academic, New York, 1959, p. 157.
16. Bender, M. L., and F. J. Kézdy: *J. Am. Chem. Soc.*, **86**: 3704 (1964).
17. Cathou, R. E., and G. G. Hammes: *J. Am. Chem. Soc.*, **87**: 4674 (1965).
18. Alberty, R. A., and G. G. Hammes: *J. Phys. Chem.*, **62**: 154 (1958).
19. Hammes, G. G.: *Nature*, **204**: 342 (1964).
20. Mintel, R., and J. Westley: *J. Biol. Chem.*, **241**: 3386 (1966).
21. Leininger, K., and J. Westley: *J. Biol. Chem.*, **243**: 1892 (1968).
22. Mintel, R., and J. Westley: *J. Biol. Chem.*, **241**: 3381 (1966).
23. Laidler, K. J.: *Arch. Biochem.*, **30**: 226 (1951).
24. Cleland, W. W.: *Advan. Enzymol.*, **29**: 1 (1967).
25. Horowitz, P., and J. Westley: Manuscript in preparation.
26. Wang, S.-F., and M. Volini: *J. Biol. Chem.* **243**: 5465 (1968).
27. Sörbo, B.: *Acta Chem. Scand.*, **16**: 2455 (1962).

14

IDENTIFICATION
OF SPECIFIC GROUPS:
USE OF pH VARIATION
AND "GROUP-SPECIFIC" REAGENTS

Having established some rather general properties of the catalytically significant groups in an enzyme, including perhaps net ionic charge and degree of nucleophilicity or electrophilicity, the investigator generally craves to complete the identification. This process is probably never as easy as it appears in anticipation, but approaching it from a sound basic understanding of the conditions required to isolate the individual reactions in that particular mechanism diminishes the problems greatly. In what follows we shall often find that correct interpretation of experimental data obtained with inhibiting or inactivating reagents is simply not possible without a knowledge of at least the formal catalytic mechanism.

In one way the reversible reagents, including H^+, are more useful than those that inactivate the enzyme permanently since the former permit kinetic isolation of the reaction in which the enzymic group takes part. On the other hand, irreversible reagents afford the greater certainty in identifying the enzymic group affected. This is especially true when the bond formed with the enzyme can withstand hydrolysis, permitting isolation of the modified residue, as in the highly specific reaction of organophosphorus compounds with the reactive serine residue in the active sites of many hydrolases.

pH EFFECTS

From much that has appeared in previous chapters, it must be clear that ionizable groups play critical roles in enzymic catalysis. Moreover, since proton association and dissociation could be treated exactly like any other modifier reactions (Chap. 4), nobody should be

154

surprised to find analytical use being made of pH effects for the purpose of detecting ionizable groups significant for enzyme activity. A kind of kinetic technology has grown up around this usage and wherever individual rate or equilibrium constants in a mechanism can be secured across a pH range, useful and sometimes highly specific information about participating groups is made available.

IONIZING GROUPS OF ENZYMES

The average pK ranges for ionizable groups of proteins are shown in Fig. 22 superposed on a typical protein titration curve. It should be noted about this compilation that the ranges are broad and, even so, not rigorously all-encompassing. A further fact of note is that the pK values do not coincide with those for the free amino acids, since the electrostatic and the inductive effects of neighboring groups are very much altered by incorporation into the peptide chain. The broad ranges given relate to the fact that the globular protein can provide a variety of environments for ionizable groups both in terms of electronic effects and in terms of polarity of the medium. Still, it would be surprising to find a protein carboxyl group with a pK of 6 or a tyrosyl phenolic pK at 8, so that this chart can serve as a kind of practical guide to what to expect. Moreover, since the heats of ionization for these groups also differ (parenthetical numbers in Fig. 22) and since the pK values differ as well in sensitivity to ionic strength and dielectric constant, enough experimental parameters are often available to permit reasonable inferences regarding the identities of active groups. Thus a pK at 5 might be a high carboxyl ionization or a low imidazolium. Normally, one would expect to be able to make this distinction on the basis of the variation of pK with temperature, since the heats of ionization of these residues differ so greatly. Further, a pK of 10.5 might be either a lysl ε-amino group or a tyrosyl phenolic hydroxyl but the distinction could probably be made on the basis of variation with ionic strength, as pK values of hydroxyl (and carboxyl) groups are very sensitive to this solution parameter while those of ammonium groups are not.

PLOTTING FORMS

Although H^+ inhibition or activation can be handled like that of any other modifier, Dixon (1) pointed out that evaluation of pK′ values can most easily be made from logarithmic plots. To cite the

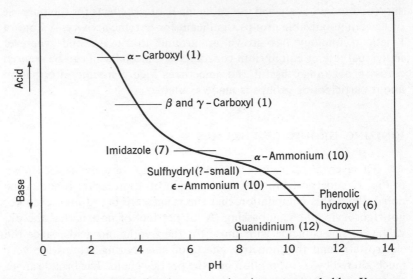

FIG. 22.   Typical protein titration curve, showing most probable pK ranges for the ionizable groups. Numbers in parentheses are approximate enthalpies of ionization in kcal/mole for the specified groups.

simplest example, taking the logarithms of both sides of Eq. (32) of Chap. 4 yields

$$\log v_0 = \log (k_{+2} E_0 A) - \log (K_m + A) - \log \left(1 + \frac{K_a}{H}\right)$$

Clearly, when $H \gg K_a$, the last term becomes zero, i.e., there is no dependence of $\log v_0$ on pH. When, however, $H \ll K_a$, the last term varies directly as pH, i.e., $\log v_0$ is simply proportional to pH under these conditions.

These ideas have been refined to show that plots of logarithmic functions of V/K_m, V, K_s, and K_m against pH must all be composed of linear segments having small integral slopes connected by curved transitional regions. Extrapolation of the linear segments to points of intersection yields pK' values for groups involved in some way in the activity.

Where $\log V$ is plotted as a function of pH, as one might expect, the ionization behavior of groups affecting the unimolecular step in the simple one-substrate mechanism is reflected. When $\log V/K_m$ is plotted against pH, again as expected (see the last section of Chap. 4), only groups significant for complex formation will be seen, i.e., groups of either the free enzyme or substrate. It is interesting that both types of effects can be seen in logarithmic plots of the Michaelis constant. The forms of these plots are illustrated in Fig. 23.

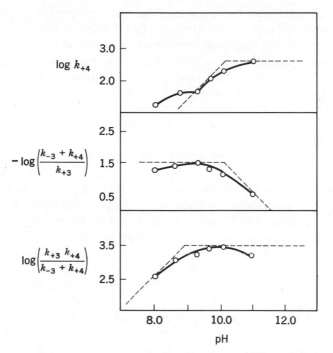

FIG. 23. Logarithmic pH plots, illustrating the technique for determining pK values of ionizable groups in the enzyme, the substrate and the enzyme-substrate complex significant for activity. The data shown represent the interaction of lipoate with the rhodanese-sulfur substituted enzyme according to the formal mechanism of Fig. 19, Chapter 9. The logarithmic values plotted are related to the log V, pK_m, and log (V/K_m) of the classical one-substrate treatment. (Adapted from M. Volini and J. Westley, *J. Biol. Chem.*, **241**: 5168 (1966). Used by permission.)

The promulgation of these forms, complete with pat rules for their interpretation, gave rise to a certain amount of uncritical work. Some of this seems simply to have been laziness, involving mainly the failure to secure true initial velocities in steady-state work or to do complete kinetic experiments at all pH values used. Most of it, however, suffered from a more fundamental problem, uncritical application to two-substrate systems of an analytical scheme derived for a simple one-substrate model.[1] Nevertheless, a calm look at this approach to detecting specific groups shows it to be potentially a fine tool. Just as the use of any other

[1] This is a very serious problem. Simple plotting of Michaelis constants and maximum velocities in multisubstrate systems can lead to substantial errors in the pK values obtained. The difficulty is the kinetic complexity of these systems, which as we have seen causes Michaelis constants, for example, to be complicated composites involving many rate constants.

inhibitor or activator can illuminate the nature of groups for which it has known affinities, so can the use of H^+. What is required here as anywhere else is a reasonable assurance of proper kinetic isolation of the reaction parameters. The work can be done by modern steady-state methods, by transient state kinetics, by relaxation techniques, or by any other methodology permitting determination of individual rate constants or known combinations of rate constants at several pH values. Failure to do enough work to separate the constants adequately gives results that properly cannot be interpreted.

The careful use of pH-activity data has been of great value in analyzing the mechanisms of the hydrolases. The opportunity to isolate individual kinetic events by use of stopped-flow techniques, steady-state analysis, or relaxation techniques has provided some definitive results. This is especially true for trypsin and chymotrypsin with some of their substrates (2,3). The participation of histidyl residues in both the acylation and deacylation steps of the chymotrypsin mechanism was first known from such evidence. Some steady-state data have also yielded useful conclusions for non-hydrolases and this source of evidence may be expected to increase fairly rapidly now that two-substrate formal analysis is becoming common. The Alberty group has done a very careful study of the pK values of the binding groups in fumarase and of their enthalpies of ionization (4). The pH-dependent reversible dimerization of rhodanese (5) was first suspected on the basis of the pH dependence of $K_m^{SSO_3^-}$, in conjunction with the other evidence on the mechanism of this enzyme (6).

One of the most detailed analyses of pH effects yet to appear in the literature is Hammes' temperature jump study of the elementary events occurring in the interaction of ribonuclease and cytidine-3'-phosphate in the presence of a colorimetric indicator (7). The evidence obtained in this study permitted inferences to be made regarding three groups in the active site. The three pK' values were 5, 6, and 6.7. Study of these values as a function of temperature showed that the group with the lowest pK' is a carboxyl group (low temperature dependence) and that with the highest pK' is an imidazolium (high temperature dependence). The group with the pK' of 6, however, was (and is) a puzzle. The lack of temperature dependence suggested a carboxyl group, the pK' itself an imidazolium. These investigators argue for an imidazolium with an abnormal $\Delta H_{ionization}$ but concede that the case is really indeterminant from these data alone. Furthermore, a formal mechanism in detail including isomerization reactions of free enzyme and enzyme-product complexes was indicated. The high level of kinetic resolution attained in this analysis lends some credence to the speculative chemical mechanism offered, although there appears to be some question that all of the isomerization reactions are in fact parts of the catalytic reaction sequence.

OTHER REVERSIBLE REACTIONS

In general, it appears that little effort has been spent in developing reversible reagents for specific groups, or more generally, reversible reagents with predictable affinities for particular groups to be used in a manner analogous to the use of hydronium ions indicated above. Most research on reversible agents has concentrated on substrate analogues. The successful inhibitors have generally been duly classified as to their degree of competitiveness with a substrate. Relatively few, however, have been considered group-specific reagents in the same sense as the irreversible modifiers. Nevertheless, they have the great advantage that they permit ready determination of the kinetic locus of action. For example, aromatic charge-transfer acceptors can be used where a tryptophyl residue is implicated in the mechanism. If the formal mechanism is well understood, a rather simple kinetic experiment can yield information about the step in which the tryptophyl residue participates and, hence, about the role of this group in the catalysis. Similarly, coordinating agents for metal ions can be used reversibly (even chelating agents, in cases where the metal ion is bound very firmly to the enzyme) but the observation can be complicated by the irreversible reaction in which the ion is removed from the enzyme. Metal ions themselves may be used as reversible reagents, too, although the specificity obtained is less. Sulfhydryl groups and imidazoles have strong affinities for most metal ions but so do both carboxyl and amino groups and even peptide bonds, so that the chelation possibilities are many.

A further instance of reversible reagents may arise out of developments in fluorescence methodology as applied to proteins. Reagents like toluidinylnaphthalene sulfonate (8) that associate only with hydrophobic groups (and fluoresce only when so associated) should be considered for use in this category.

IRREVERSIBLE REACTIONS

Most of the so-called group-specific reagents react irreversibly with the residues they attack. Since many non-specific treatments are capable of inactivating enzymes, considerable caution is required in the use of irreversible reagents. There are, in fact, two kinds of difficulties with such studies: (a) things that should react do not, and (b) things that should not react do.

The former category of trouble is the result of the occurrence of different chemical environments in a globular protein, so that a group that is "buried" from the point of view of the potential inactivating reagent may be both readily accessible to and very reactive toward a substrate or a different reagent. Failure to inactivate, then, can only be useful in drawing conclusions if it can also be shown that reaction has occurred. Similarly, the latter category of trouble occurs because of the increased reactivity of some residues, which then react with reagents that they normally would not react with. As examples, note the recent report of Takahashi et al. (9) regarding a carboxyl group in ribonuclease T_1 that reacted with iodoacetate, normally a reagent for much stronger nucleophiles like sulfhydryl or imidazole groups. There is also the report of Brewer and Riehm (10) concerning the reaction of N-ethylmaleimide with a lysyl ε-amino group rather than the sulfhydryl group for which it is supposed to be specific.

The above examples are cited to emphasize that no reagent is absolutely specific. Generally it is essential to demonstrate analytically which residue has been modified. As a matter of fact, even this may not suffice, although it is widely believed to be adequate. Consider the experience of Wang and Volini (11), following up B. Davidson's preliminary observation that rhodanese was very sensitive to chloro-dinitrobenzene, presumed to be a reagent for lysyl ε-amino groups. These investigators found that no residue had been substituted in the enzyme inactivated with this reagent and even dinitrobenzene itself was found to inactivate the enzyme. The inactivation was ultimately traced to an unexpected oxidation of an enzymic sulfhydryl group by dinitrophenyl compounds. However, if Wang and Volini had found a dinitrophenyl lysine in the hydrolysate, they would have been in accord with the usual practice if they had concluded that this was an essential residue.

In view of such experiences, it appears that we need some minimum standards to be used in identifying possible active site groups by use of group reagents. The following criteria are suggested:

1. The substrate should "protect" the activity, i.e., the substrate and reagent should be mutually exclusive to some extent. This means that some support for the proposal is obtained when the action of a reversible reagent is competitive with respect to a substrate or when the reaction of an irreversible reagent is slowed by the presence of a substrate.

2. There should be correlation of activity loss with loss of a single group. Such a correlation may be made on either a kinetic or a stoichiometric basis. Ray and Koshland (12,13) have stressed the value of the kinetic approach; a convincing example of the stoichiometric approach can be found in the study of an essential sulfhydryl group by Wang and Volini (11).

3. "Dummy reagents" should have no effect on the activity. It seems essential always to test as potential inhibitors or inactivators compounds having chemical and physical properties as nearly like the reagent as possible, with the exception of the one property that results in the specific action of the reagent. Considerable care must be exercised to ensure that this is done properly. For example, in the work cited above, where use of the dummy reagent dinitrobenzene provided insight into the action of chlorodinitrobenzene, dinitrophenol as a dummy reagent would have failed, as it does not inactivate the enzyme under comparable conditions.

4. Wherever possible, regeneration of the activity should be sought by appropriate specific reversing procedures. Tests where this is possible are preferable over those where it is not as this is the only reasonable control to eliminate the possibility that general denaturation is the cause of inactivation. Thus, acetylation of tyrosyl hydroxyl groups with acetylimidazole may be preferable to iodination of the ring, as the substituent acetyl group hydrolyzes off spontaneously at slightly alkaline pH. Similarly, inactivation of an enzyme by formation of a mixed disulfide with a sulfhydryl compound is generally a more convincing single-test demonstration of an essential sulfhydryl group than is alkylation of the group with iodoacetate or N-ethylmaleimide. The former procedure allows activity to be regenerated by simple reduction but the permanent loss of activity in the latter case might have been caused by either the specific action at the sulfhydryl group found substituted or by secondary conformational alteration. Clearly, the two types of experiments are complementary.

The above points should not be taken as a set of rules for demonstrating active site groups. They are at most minimum criteria for such a claim and are intended more as an illustration of the areas in which the use of group reagents can be most definitive. It is the hope of the author that they might serve as an antidote to the overly simplistic acceptance and use of "group-specific reagents" without consideration of the many possible complexities of interpretation.

No exhaustive catalogue of group reagents will be attempted here. For a good current compilation, the reader is referred to Vol. 11 of *Methods in Enzymology*. Table 8 is presented to illustrate what a typical

TABLE 8. *Effects of Group-Specific Reagents on Rhodanese Activity*

Treatment	Result[a]	Expected Result							
		His	Cys	Tyr	Met	—COOH	—NH₃	Trypt	Denaturation
H₂O₂	+	+	+	+	+	—	—	+	+
Photooxidation	+	+	+	+	+	—	—	+	—
Diazobenzene sulfonate	—	+	—	+	—	—	—	—	—
Fluorodinitrobenzene	+	+	+	+	—	+	+	—[b]	—
Chlorodinitrobenzene	+	—	—[c]	—	—	+	+	—[b]	—
Dinitrobenzene	+	—	—[c]	—	—	—	—	—[b]	—
Mercuribenzoate	—	—	+[d]	—	—	—	—	—	—
Iodoacetate	+	+	+	—	+	—	—	—	—
N-Ethylmaleimide	+	—	+	—	—	—	—	—	—
Mercaptoethanol + O₂	+	—	+	—	—	—	—	—	—
N-Bromosuccinimide	+	—	—	—	—	—	—	+	—
Charge transfer acceptors	+	—	—	—	—	—	—	+	—

[a] + signifies either inactivation or competitive inhibition; — signifies no effect.

[b] The tryptophyl residue is probably involved in complexing the dinitroaryl compounds that oxidize the sulfhydryl group.

[c] The dinitroaryl compounds oxidize the active site sulfhydryl group in rhodanese, forming inactive rhodanese dimer, although they do not readily oxidize other sulfhydryl compounds.

[d] The sulfhydryl groups of native rhodanese seem to be inaccessible to mercuribenzoate. In any case, the assay reagents react with this compound.

study might involve, the overall interpretation there being one of active site involvement of cysteinyl and tryptophyl residues and probable noninvolvement of the other residues indicated.

BIFUNCTIONAL REAGENTS

Recently there has been a growing realization that the most efficient use of monofunctional group reagents is in conjunction with bifunctional reagents to secure information relating to the proximity of different essential groups in the globular structure of an enzyme. Often this is the only way to gain assurance that an esssential group is in the active site rather than fulfilling some structural role (14). Thus a competitive inhibitor with action at one type of enzymic group can often slow down the attack by even an irreversible reagent that has specificity for a different group when the two groups affected are both in the same active center. When this occurs, confirmation of the inference of proximity can be secured if both types of reagents can be built into the same molecule. Under these circumstances, the presence of the reversible component can enhance rather than diminish the action of the other.

Rhodanese again provides an example. One of the two sulfhydryl groups of the enzyme monomer is clearly essential for the activity (11), as discussed in the preceding section. There is also a tryptophyl residue whose destruction leads to loss of activity (15). Moreover, reagents that form reversible complexes with indoles, including both pyridinium cations (15) and aromatic anions rather generally (11), are strictly competitive inhibitors with respect to the thiosulfate. One may then inquire whether these two essential residues are very near one another in the active enzyme, as this question will surely bear on any chemical mechanism for the catalysis that one wishes to propose. Two facts lead to the conclusion that they are in fact very near. First, the aromatics that serve as competitive inhibitors for the catalyzed reaction also inhibit attack on the essential sulfhydryl group. Second, aromatic oxidizing agents (dinitrophenyl compounds) that have low reactivity with typical sulfhydryl groups, but would be expected to form complexes with the tryptophyl residue, oxidize the essential sulfhydryl of this enzyme very rapidly. The inference that the essential tryptophyl and sulfhydryl residues are close together, and at least close to the substrate binding site for thiosulfate, is difficult to avoid. The use of bifunctional reagents for such purposes is becoming rather widespread. Shaw (16) has compiled a group of "site specific" reagents for chymotrypsin and trypsin, and Wold (17) has summarized the use of bifunctional reagents for use in making covalent cross links between peptide chains.

ENVIRONMENTALLY SENSITIVE REAGENTS

It is commonplace that the absorption and emission spectra of organic compounds are sensitive to the immediate physical environment. The fine structure of absorption spectra observed for aromatic compounds in nonpolar solvents is absent from spectra of the same compounds in water. Similarly, intensities of fluorescence are diminished in polar solvents, sometimes very markedly. Such observations have suggested the possibility that the nature of the physical environments inside proteins could be inferred from spectral measurements of specific groups attached for this purpose. Koshland has designated such substituents "reporter groups" (18).

An example of such usage is in the application of 2-hydroxy-5-nitrobenzyl bromide, a reagent with specificity for tryptophyl residues (19). Where this reagent can be reacted with a tryptophyl residue near an active site, the influence of substrate attachment can be seen. A number of applications of this basic idea have recently been made (20,21). The ultraviolet absorption spectrum in the product of the reaction of fluorescein mercuric acetate with the rhodanese active site sulfhydryl group has been used to demonstrate the hydrophobic character of that region of the enzyme molecule (22). This result is in accord with the apolar nature of the active site peptides obtained from this enzyme by tryptic digestion (23).

GENERAL REFERENCES

Laidler, K. J.: *The Chemical Kinetics of Enzyme Action*, Oxford, London, 1958.
Dixon, M., and E. C. Webb: *Enzymes*, Academic, New York, 1964.
Hirs, C. H. W.: *Methods Enzymol.*, **11**, 1967.
Baker, B. R.: *Design of Active-Site-Directed Irreversible Enzyme Inhibitors*, Wiley, New York, 1967.

SPECIFIC REFERENCES

1. Dixon, M.: *Biochem. J.*, **55**: 161 (1953).
2. Bender, M. L., and E. T. Kaiser: *J. Am. Chem. Soc.*, **84**: 2556 (1962).
3. Bender, M. L., and F. J. Kézdy: *J. Am. Chem. Soc.*, **86**: 3704 (1964).

4. Brant, D. A., L. B. Barnett, and R. A. Alberty: *J. Am. Chem. Soc.*, **79**: 1526 (1957).
5. Volini, M., F. DeToma, and J. Westley: *J. Biol. Chem.*, **242**: 5220 (1967).
6. Volini, M., and J. Westley: *J. Biol. Chem.*, **241**: 5168 (1966).
7. Cathou, R. E., and G. G. Hammes: *J. Am. Chem. Soc.*, **87**: 4669, 4674 (1965).
8. McClure, W. O., and G. M. Edelman: *Biochemistry*, **5**: 1908 (1966).
9. Takahashi, K., S. Moore, and W. H. Stein: *Federation Proc.*, **26**: 601 (1967).
10. Brewer, C. F., and J. P. Riehm; *Anal. Biochem.*, **18**: 248 (1967).
11. Wang, S.-F., and M. Volini, : *J. Biol. Chem.*, **243**: 5465 (1968).
12. Ray, W. J., Jr., and D. E. Koshland, Jr.: *J. Biol. Chem.*, **237**: 2493 (1962).
13. Koshland, D. E., Jr., D. H. Strumeyer, and W. J. Ray, Jr.: *Brookhaven Symp. Biol.*, **15**: 101 (1962).
14. Koshland, D. E., Jr.: *Advan. Enzymol.*, **22**: 45 (1960).
15. Davidson, B., and J. Westley: *J. Biol. Chem.*, **240**: 4463 (1965).
16. Shaw, E.: *Methods Enzymol.*, **11**: 677 (1967).
17. Wold, F.: *Methods Enzymol.*, **11**: 617 (1967).
18. Horton, H. R., and D. E. Koshland, Jr.: *Methods Enzymol.*, **11**: 556, 856, 857 (1967).
19. Horton, H. R., and D. E. Koshland, Jr.: *J. Am. Chem. Soc.*, **87**: 1126 (1965).
20. Berliner, L. J., and H. M. McConnell: *Proc. Natl. Acad. Sci. U.S.*, **55**: 708 (1966).
21. Conway, A., and D. E. Koshland, Jr.: *Biochim. Biophys. Acta*, **133**: 593 (1967).
22. Horowitz, P., and J. Westley: Manuscript in preparation.
23. DeToma, F., and J. Westley: Manuscript in preparation.

PART IV

METABOLIC CONTROL AT THE ENZYME LEVEL

By and large, enzymology has been slow in according recognition to the atypical behavior of enzymes that are involved in metabolic control. Enzymologists have been quick to work with "linear" systems, i.e., those yielding good straight lines in the linear plotting forms, and reluctant to approach the much greater complexity implicit in other behavior. Now, however, so many enzymes have been shown to yield sigmoid rather than hyperbolic plots of initial velocity against concentration of substrate added, or some other evidence of regulation, that we are certainly obliged to consider the possible bases for such effects. Furthermore, in view of the obvious biochemical importance of regulatory systems, we must also go on briefly to consider where regulatory, and especially self-regulatory, behavior might be seen in the simplest kinds of systems involving more than one enzyme. In both of these main areas, however, we can deal only with the most elementary considerations as a general introduction to topics somewhat distant from the main theme of this book.

15

REGULATORY ENZYMES
AND SIGMOID KINETICS

The fundamental observation on which most thought regarding regulatory enzymes has been based is that of "sigmoid kinetics." This term refers to the fact that for many enzymes under certain conditions plots of initial velocity against substrate concentration are not rectangular hyperbolas through the origin (Fig. 24). This behavior is found most frequently for enzymes at branch points in biosynthetic pathways or enzymes for which, at least in retrospect, a role in regulation of metabolic energy flow makes sense. Intuitively, it makes regulatory sense to move the region in which velocity is most sensitive to substrate concentration out to the physiological concentration range. One of several possibilities achieving this result is the introduction of sigmoidicity. The particular conditions found to yield regulatory behavior commonly include the presence of an "effector" molecule, which may be an activator or an inhibitor of the activity (a positive or negative effector, Fig. 24) and which may or may not also be a substrate of the enzyme.

Much thought in this field appears to have been based on an analogy between the nonhyperbolic curves for velocity as a function of substrate concentration obtained with regulatory enzymes and the sigmoid oxygen-binding saturation curves for hemoglobin. Since in the latter case, oxygen binding is correlated with a conformational difference inferred from the different X-ray diffraction patterns given by crystals of hemoglobin and oxyhemoglobin, a similar structural basis has been presumed for regulatory enzymes. It remains to be seen whether this analogy is a fortunate one.

There seem to be at least six different kinds of general mechanisms for sigmoid behavior, some of them rather trivial and easy to distinguish, others of fundamental significance perhaps, but more

169

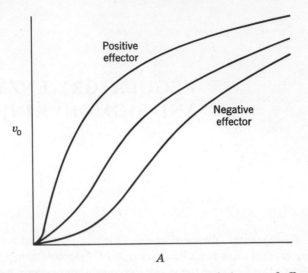

$$v_0$$

FIG. 24. Sigmoid kinetics in the presence and absence of effectors.

difficult to detect with certainty. We shall examine each briefly and go
on to consider a further kind of regulatory behavior that does not give
conventional sigmoid kinetics in the same sense.

ERRORS IN SUBSTRATE CONCENTRATION

As we have seen in Chap. 4, markedly nonlinear double reciprocal
plots are obtained in kinetic experiments in the presence of a modifier
that reacts irreversibly with the substrate that is varied in concentration.
Figure 25 shows this form and also the sigmoid plot obtained when the
same data are plotted as v_0 against $[A]$. This is surely a trivial cause of
sigmoidicity, where the "effector" molecule or an impurity in the
effector solution simply reacts with a stoichiometric amount of the
varied substrate. An exactly similar phenomenon occurs when either
the effector solution or the enzyme solution contains a quantity of
substrate sufficient to be a significant increment in total substrate at the
lower concentrations tested. This again is a trivial cause of nonlinear
behavior. Precisely because they are trivial, of course, these possible
causes must be borne in mind. Especially in complex reaction media or
in the use of enzymes not very highly purified, an effect of this sort
could arise easily and would certainly wreak havoc on regulatory
interpretation. Work with carefully purified chemicals and thorough

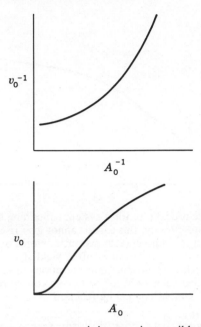

FIG. 25.   Plots for a system containing an irreversible substrate modifier.

kinetic investigation of all concentration parameters should ordinarily make it possible to avoid these unwelcome complications.

MIXED ENZYMES

When the enzyme solution used contains more than one enzyme acting on the varied substrate, it is also possible to obtain data that describe a sigmoid saturation curve. Figure 26 shows typical data obtainable with a mixture containing two enzymes that compete for the varied substrate. In this case the "effector" would simply be an activator for the second enzyme. This cause of such behavior is ordinarily easy to detect as a discrepancy between the kinetics of substrate utilization and the kinetics of formation of all the expected products. It is most easily avoided, of course, by working with highly purified enzyme preparations that have been carefully tested for interfering impurities and by following both substrate utilization and product appearance.

Possibly this cause of nonlinear behavior, like that in the previous section, is a trivial one physiologically—no more than a trap for the unwary or lazy enzymologist. On the other hand, enzymes *in vivo*

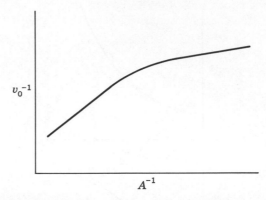

FIG. 26.   Double reciprocal plot for a system containing two enzymes acting on the same substrate. Strictly, this cause cannot give rise to sigmoidicity in the plot of v_0 against A. In practice, however, mixtures of enzymes that convert the substrate to different products often yield sigmoids when velocities are determined by following product concentration. In such cases, the cause of apparent diminished velocity at low substrate concentration is the utilization of substrate by a rapid competing reaction.

probably are engaged in competition for scarce substrates, notably coenzymes, and this mechanism could in fact relate to control systems in the cell.

NONLINEAR TWO-SUBSTRATE MECHANISMS

Even where only a single enzyme is present, we know from the considerations of Chap. 8 that nonlinear behavior can arise anywhere that there are two forms of enzyme with which the varied substrate can react. For example, two-substrate ternary complex mechanisms can give nonlinear behavior when the order of attachment is random (yielding both free E and the complex (EB) with which A may react) unless equilibrium conditions obtain. Under some circumstances, the plots of v_0 against A will be sigmoid. Any compound, then, that acts in a ternary complex enzyme mechanism in such a way as to accelerate the breakdown of the ternary complex could appear as an "effector" by converting an equilibrium system to a nonequilibrium system.

The foregoing is only one example from a rather large field of possibilities of this general sort (1). Actually, the concept of linear and branched mechanisms is applicable as well to the additional causes outlined in the subsequent sections. Our aim in this section, as in the former two, has been to show that there can occur rather nonspecific and perhaps trivial causes for the kind of kinetic behavior that has sometimes been accepted uncritically as evidence for regulatory function or, worse, as evidence for a particular physical structure of an enzyme.

MULTIPLE INTERACTING SUBSTRATE SITES

Serious consideration of mechanisms for genuine regulatory behavior should probably begin with a study of the possibilities inherent in multiple equivalent binding sites for substrate on an enzyme molecule. The Hill equation (2) is much used to express this idea. Following the treatment of Atkinson *et al.* (3), suppose that there are n binding sites and that equilibrium conditions obtain. Then $E + nA \overset{K_1}{\rightleftharpoons} (EA_n) \overset{k_{+2}}{\rightarrow} E + nX$, and

$$K_1 = \frac{EA^n}{(EA_n)} \tag{55}$$

with K_1 thus set up as a dissociation constant analogous to K_s. If in addition it is assumed that binding is highly "cooperative" (i.e., that each substrate molecule bound increases the association constant for the next), the only enzymic forms present at significant concentrations will be the free enzyme and the fully loaded enzyme.

$$E_0 = E + (EA_n) \tag{56}$$

The implication is then that the total velocity of the catalyzed reaction can be accounted for by the decomposition of the fully loaded enzyme.

$$v_0 = k_{+2}(EA_n) \tag{57}$$

Then

$$V = k_{+2} E_0 \tag{58}$$

and, combining Eqs. (56)–(58),

$$k_{+2} E = V - v_0 \tag{59}$$

It follows that

$$\frac{(EA_n)}{E} = \frac{v_0}{V - v_0} = \frac{A^n}{K_1} \tag{60}$$

The usual form of the Hill equation is obtained by taking the logarithm of Eq. (60) to obtain a slope-intercept form

$$\log\left(\frac{v_0}{V - v_0}\right) = n \log A - \log K_1$$

One plots $\log[v_0/(V - v_0)]$ against $\log A$, obtaining a straight line with slope n and ordinate intercept $(-\log K_1)$.

Several features of this treatment need to be noted. The assumptions on which it is based are arbitrary and very restrictive. In applying the equation it is necessary to point out that we do not actually know what n means. It must refer to some mixed function of the number of binding sites and degree of site interaction. The value of n approaches 1 as site interaction disappears.[1]

Similarly, it would be erroneous to conclude that K_1 has a well-defined meaning, even as an overall equilibrium constant according to the definition of Eq. (55). As Hill (2) and Atkinson et al. (3) have pointed out, the Hill equation is a generalized Henri equation, subject to the same general objection that it assumes equilibrium conditions among all enzyme-containing species. The actual meaning of K_1 must, then, be that of a complex steady-state constant. Its value will certainly change as substrate affinity is altered but can also be changed by alteration of the rate constants for steps not involved in binding. Effectors that change the half-saturating substrate concentrations without changing V presumably do exert their effects on the binding step but of course it does not follow that the equilibrium assumption is correct. The same observations are equally in accord with the extreme opposite assumption (corresponding to completely irreversible substrate binding) or any intermediate general case.

Granting, then, some reservations about the assumptions involved in the Hill equation, it is surprising how well some enzymes appear to fulfill the necessary conditions for fairly simple interpretation in these terms. One excellent example is the study of yeast NAD-isocitrate dehydrogenase by Atkinson et al. (3). In this work the Hill plots for all substrates and effectors are linear with integral slopes under a variety of experimental conditions, suggesting that in this case n might really represent the number of sites, i.e., that cooperativity is very large. In fact, assignment of the indicated numbers of equivalent sites for the substrates and effectors and assumption of an interaction factor ≥ 20 for the substrate sites (at least twentyfold increase in affinity constant for each subsequent isocitrate bound), along with a surprisingly few other minor assumptions, permitted construction of a kinetic model that fits the rather complex regulatory kinetic data for this enzyme very well. Minor adjustments of the assumed interaction parameters, for example, obviously could yield fits to the experimental data to any degree of closeness. While it is clear that such a simple treatment will not serve for all regulatory enzymes, the existence of such a "pure

---

[1] That is, multivalent enzymes in which there is no site interaction give normal, hyperbolic plots of v_0 against A. It is not possible, in fact, to distinguish kinetically how many independent catalytic sites an enzyme molecule has.

case" suggests that factors involved in this treatment might be major elements in much regulatory behavior. It is noteworthy that this model, unlike some of the others described below, also fits the data in not demanding a decrease in sigmoidicity as the concentration of positive effector is increased. Plots of data for enzyme fully saturated with positive effector are as sigmoid as any others.

It should also be noted that the foregoing model does not necessarily imply any particular physical mechanism for the site interactions. Its authors presumed that it might involve a kind of extension of Koshland's "induced fit" hypothesis in which complexing with a substrate molecule caused a conformational change resulting somehow in the increased binding affinity for subsequent substrate molecules. Conformation change is also a feature of the other, more complex models for regulation kinetics discussed below.

SEPARATE SUBSTRATE AND EFFECTOR SUBUNITS

The idea that substrate molecules and molecules of regulatory metabolites occupy distinct (rather than, say, overlapping) sites on the enzyme is suggested by the chemical dissimilarity of specific substrates and specific effectors in many cases, hence the term "allosteric" effector. Gerhart and Pardee have applied this concept to aspartate transcarbamylase, for which cytidine triphosphate (CTP) is a negative effector and ATP a positive one (4). This work has culminated in the isolation of separate catalytic and effector-binding subunits (5). Separated catalytic subunits show normal (nonsigmoid) kinetics and are insensitive to CTP or ATP. The regulatory enzyme can be reconstituted from the separated subunits. This is, then, an exceedingly clear-cut case involving separate sites and participation of conformational change through interaction of subunits. It is not yet clear how general these features are in the action of regulatory enzymes.

Frieden (6,7) has undertaken an interesting theoretical development of the separate sites idea. The first of these papers deals with what happens to the theoretical kinetic behavior when you add an effector and an effector site to the basic one-substrate mechanism. This treatment yields regulatory behavior without any recourse whatever to multiple interacting substrate sites. The second paper increases the complexity to the multisite level and makes some comparisons among the various models. This work provides one means of making some mechanistic distinctions without invoking inactive subunits. The model proposed is an extension of the Monod model (cited below) to include some substrate binding by subunits as well as by their condensed forms.

MULTIPLE IDENTICAL SUBUNITS WITH NONCOOPERATIVE BINDING

As an attempt to strike through to a single model that would account for regulatory behavior generally, Monod *et al.* suggested one in which each enzymic subunit had one substrate-binding site and one effector site (8). The effector action determined which of two conformational forms was taken by the condensed form of the subunits. One form had greater substrate-binding affinity than the other. This combination of properties is capable of generating sigmoid behavior and the general model fits the behavior shown by a substantial number of enzymes, including those cited by Monod *et al.* (8), glutamic dehydrogenase (9), the mammary glucose-6-phosphate dehydrogenase (10) and yeast glyceraldehyde phosphate dehydrogenase (11). Nevertheless, it cannot serve as an entirely general model. It does not seem capable of accounting for the aspartate transcarbamylase case cited above.[2] Furthermore, since all the enzyme should be in one form at positive effector saturation, the model predicts that kinetics should be normal rather than sigmoid under these conditions. In fact, as Atkinson has pointed out (15), both the yeast isocitric dehydrogenase, discussed above and *E. coli* phosphofructokinase (16) clearly violate this prediction, and there seems to be no other way of distinguishing kinetically between this model and the more general multiple site cooperative model.

Koshland *et al.* (17) have considered four of the possible interaction arrays for four subunits, each with a single substrate-binding site. Subunits could exist in two forms: binding and nonbinding. The prior treatments of Monod (8) and of Atkinson (3) were deliberately subsumed in this consideration and a careful comparison of the kinetic consequences yielded two general findings of considerable note: (a) Systems with interacting subunits *can* give normal, hyperbolic saturation curves. (An observation to pair off with the implication of the earlier sections of this chapter that sigmoid curves *can* be obtained by various means not involving subunits or interacting substrate sites.) (b) Many models that appear distinct may be capable of fitting the same set of empirical data (of the saturation curve variety) about equally well; i.e., kinetic analysis alone may not ever suffice to distinguish among the possible formal mechanisms for regulation of the enzyme level.

---

[2] A recent series of three papers, however, has sought to reconcile these in terms of a revised model for aspartate transcarbamylase (12–14).

RESPONSE TO A CONCENTRATION RATIO

Atkinson (18,19) has recently examined the consequences of varying the concentration of substrate at a fixed total concentration of substrate plus product in systems where the product is a competitive inhibitor. The model involved here is simply a one-site enzyme molecule with binding competition between substrate and product, clearly a well-known phenomenon. What is new is consideration in terms of a fixed total supply of the competitors. That is, where the overall reaction is $A \rightarrow X$, initial velocities are obtained as a function of A where $(A + X)$ is kept constant. This is the kind of situation in which coenzymes find themselves, in rapid turnover that results in an interconversion of forms which is much faster than either the synthesis or the degradation of the basic structure. Atkinson and his co-workers show that the result is a very sensitive response (i.e., steep sigmoid behavior) at each fixed concentration level. It is pointed out that this is the expected behavior for a velocity response to a concentration *ratio*. The particular application made is to metabolic energy regulation, where it is proposed that all enzymes utilizing ATP may show this type of response to the "energy charge" of the cell. Energy charge is defined as half the average number of anhydride phosphates per adenosine, thus providing a scale from zero (all AMP) to 1 (all ATP) for any total pool size.

Both rat liver citrate cleavage enzyme (18) and *E. coli* phosphoribosylpyrophosphate synthetase (19) were found to display this type of behavior, where ADP is the ATP competitor in both cases, although AMP is the immediate product of the reaction catalyzed by the latter enzyme. The sensitive response to ATP concentration generated by this means supplies an attractive general control mechanism for conservation of metabolic energy supply, a control on which the "feedback" mechanisms of energy demand may be superposed.

GENERAL REFERENCES

Atkinson, D. E.: *Ann. Rev. Biochem.*, **35**: (1966).
Stadtman, E. R.: *Advan. Enzymol.*, **28**: (1966).

SPECIFIC REFERENCES

1. Sweeny, J. R., and J. R. Fisher: *Biochemistry*, **7**: 561 (1968).
2. Hill, A. J.: *Biochem. J.*, **7**: 471 (1913).

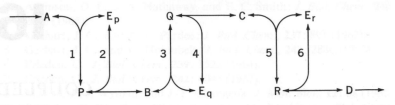

FIG. 27. A linear coupled enzyme system. E_p, E_q, and E_r are different enzymes; P, Q, and R are their complexes with substrates A, B, and C.

Figure 27 gives the model to be considered. A is constantly supplied; D is constantly removed; the system is functioning in a steady state.[2] Then

$$v = k_{+2}P - k_{-2}BE_p = k_{+4}Q - k_{-4}CE_q = \cdots \tag{61}$$

$$\frac{dP}{dt} = k_{+1}AE_p + k_{-2}BE_p - k_{-1}P - k_{+2}P \tag{62}$$

The steady-state approximation sets Eq. (62) equal to zero. The enzyme conservation equation for E_p is

$$E_{p_0} = E_p + P \tag{63}$$

Combining Eqs. (62) and (63),

$$P = \frac{E_{p_0}(k_{+1}A + k_{-2}B)}{k_{+1}A + k_{-2}B + k_{-1} + k_{+2}} \tag{64}$$

and, from Eqs. (61), (63), and (64),

$$v = E_{p_0}\left[(k_{+2} + k_{-2}B)\left(\frac{k_{+1}A + k_{-2}B}{k_{+1}A + k_{-2}B + k_{-1} + k_{+2}}\right) - k_{-2}B\right] \tag{65}$$

or in terms of K_m values for enzyme E_p

$$v = E_{p_0}\left[(k_{+2} + k_{-2}B)\left(\frac{A/K_{mp}^A + B/K_{mp}^B}{A/K_{mp}^A + B/K_{mp}^B + 1}\right) - k_{-2}B\right]$$

$$= E_{q_0}\left[(k_{+4} + k_{-4}C)\left(\frac{B/K_{mq}^B + C/K_{mq}^C}{B/K_{mq}^B + C/K_{mq}^C + 1}\right) - k_{-4}C\right]\cdots \tag{66}$$

where

$$K_{mp}^A = \frac{k_{+2} + k_{-1}}{k_{+1}}$$

and

$$K_{mp}^B = \frac{k_{+2} + k_{-1}}{k_{-2}}$$

[2] To consider this as a model related to any real system, presume the concentrations of all necessary cofactors and other auxiliary reagents to be kept constant.

It can be seen that the maximum forward velocity attainable through any segment considered individually is equal to the total concentration of that enzyme times its forward, even-numbered rate constant. That is, when A is very many times K_{mp}^A, the central term in the equation approaches unity and v approaches $k_{+2} E_{po} = V$. The maximum velocity attainable by the system as a whole is thus limited by the enzyme having the smallest maximum velocity as ordinarily defined. The concentrations of the intermediates reacting with all other enzymes in the coupled system will attain maximum values yielding this same velocity with their respective enzymes. Extraneous addition to the system of *any* of the intermediates can thus yield at most a transient perturbation in concentrations and *no* permanent change in overall velocity. This very simple coupled system has some intrinsic self-regulatory properties.

This point is further emphasized by considering the action of inhibitors on a steady-state coupled system. If E_q is the rate-limiting step, for example, and a noncompetitive inhibitor (affecting mainly V) for E_q is introduced, the velocity will tend to diminish, but note that the perturbation will have a characteristic form. B will tend to accumulate, with two results: (a) The $k_{+3} B$ reaction will tend to increase in velocity, approaching absolute saturation more closely, i.e., the system moves to minimize the velocity change. (b) The $k_{-2} B$ reaction also increases in velocity, tending to slow the net reaction from P, i.e., the E_p reaction is automatically adjusted down to the new velocity. The velocity disturbance has been minimized and the accumulation of B has been self-limiting. The system has found a new steady state.

Consider what would happen if E_q were the rate-limiting enzyme and E_r were to be partially inhibited with a reagent acting mainly on its maximum velocity. The concentration of C would rise[3] but there would be a vanishingly small effect on the overall V for the system unless the inhibition were so severe that the conversion of C to D became rate-limiting.

Furthermore, consider the case of competitive inhibitors. A competitive inhibitor for E_q, the rate-limiting enzyme, would cause accumulation of B as did the noncompetitive inhibitor considered above, but here the adjustment can be almost entirely corrective and practically no effect at all may be seen in the overall velocity. Moreover, the effects of competitive inhibitors on the other enzymes in the system may be expected to be no more substantial.

---

[3] Even this effect will be slight since the steady-state concentration of C must be below the K_m^C of E_r and the velocity of this step is thus a sensitive function of concentration.

Inhibitor analysis, then, is not simple in experimental coupled systems and very high concentrations of inhibitors may be required to achieve significant reductions in velocity. Coupled systems of this type possess excellent intrinsic self-regulation of *velocity*. Concentration levels, however, are not generally maintained by such systems (as they are by the regulatory systems of the previous chapter), and inhibitor analysis is therefore much more easily done by techniques for watching the concentration levels of the intermediates rather than the overall velocity. The concentrations of the substrate for the inhibited reaction and those before it in the sequence must increase, the concentrations of the product of the inhibited reaction and those after it in the sequence must decrease. Identifying the "crossover point" identifies the inhibited reaction.

One more question may profitably be asked of this system: What happens when one step is irreversible? Clearly, then we have a one-way street and inhibitor action might be expected to be rather different. Of the several possibilities, most turn out not to be interesting. For example, when the rate-limiting step is made irreversible (say, by discharge of a product that is maintained very near zero concentration in the solution), the action of inhibitors on V or K_m looks just like the reversible case considered above. B will tend to accumulate and the adjustments will proceed in the same way. Similarly, if the rate-limiting step is prior to the irreversible step and we inhibit the rate-limiting step, the coupled system will respond as before. It is only when the rate-limiting step *follows* the irreversible step that more interesting behavior occurs. Presume E_p of Fig. 27 to be irreversible, E_q rate limiting. If E_q is now inhibited competitively, B will accumulate, tending to relieve the inhibition; *but* if E_q is inhibited noncompetitively or uncompetitively (or irreversibly), accumulation of B can have only a very limited restoring effect. E_q is, so to speak, already working as fast as it can. Accumulation of B cannot now slow the E_p reaction and B will tend to accumulate without limit. In this one instance, a noncompetitive or uncompetitive (or irreversible) inhibition following an irreversible step, the coupled system fails at self-regulation. In short, such a system is not generally capable of maintaining a conventional steady state but "overflows."

Our findings for the simple linear coupled sequence, then, are the following: (a) Competitive inhibition of even the rate-limiting step in a reversible sequence will cause only slight alteration in velocity through the system, although it will drastically affect at least one steady-state concentration. Even noncompetitive or irreversible action of inhibitors can cause at most adjustment to a new steady state. (b) Introduction of an irreversible step destroys the self-regulating steady-state quality of the system (causes overflow) only for noncompetitive or irreversible inhibition of a rate-limiting step *following* the irreversible step.

Finally, two additional properties of coupled systems should be noted. A right combination of rate constants and enzyme concentrations could permit use of extremely labile intermediates, whose steady-state concentrations could thus be very small. Furthermore, this same purpose could be abetted by structural organization of enzymes *in vivo* so that even very small quantities of key intermediates could create effective local concentrations.

CYCLIC SYSTEMS

The foregoing story is much too simple, of course, in many ways. Biological systems are not simple linear sequences but complex networks of reactions with loops and cycles. Enzyme-catalyzed reactions do not generally involve only single substrates and products but two or three of each. Intermediates cannot be caused to pile up without limit; excretion (or death) ensues. Enzyme supply itself is not fixed but under responsive control. What we have hoped to illustrate are matters that we must expect to contend with, among many other complexities, in enzyme systems in any circumstances approaching physiological conditions.

Since one of the commonest kinetic complexities to be encountered in physiological systems is the cyclic form, let us now consider some effects of making our simple coupled reaction scheme cyclic. The system (Fig. 28) is cyclic but still open; the input of first substrate and output of last product are continuous. The only change is that one initial substrate is regenerated at a later stage. The system is in a steady-state condition and the overall velocity expression for E_q, for example, does not differ from the linear case. The other enzymes shown become two-substrate enzymes in one direction but this in itself does not alter the qualitative picture of responses.

As in the linear case, there will in general be a rate-limiting step, determined by the enzyme concentrations and unimolecular rate constants that make up the maximum velocity terms. As before, partial inhibition of the rate-limiting step will result in accumulation of some intermediate. In the cyclic case, however, the immediate consequences of this fact are not always quite the same. Let us arbitrarily designate E_p as the rate-limiting reaction. Consider, then, what happens when E_p is diminished by an irreversible agent or V is decreased by a non-competitive inhibitor. Initially, D will tend to accumulate, slowing the net clockwise velocity of the E_r step. The concentration of B will drop;

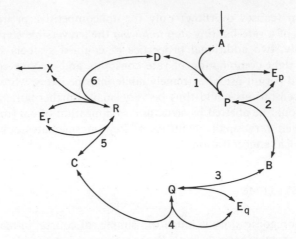

FIG. 28. A cyclic coupled enzyme system. The symbols have the same meanings as in Fig. 27.

C will tend to accumulate from the increase in D but to diminish from the decrease in B. The net change in C may be up or down but in any case by a smaller increment than B or D. Note that the crossover point still identifies the inhibited reaction but that the direction of concentration changes for reactants not adjacent to this point cannot be predicted.

Consider the case of a competitive inhibitor for E_p. D will increase until the original velocity is nearly regained; B will change rather little and C is more likely to increase than to decrease. There is nothing unique about our selection of E_p here as the rate-limiting step. Choice of any other step yields the same result.

What remains to be seen is what happens in the cyclic system when one of the steps is irreversible. Let us use E_r as the rate-limiting step in this case, as there is a product given off and its removal could be used to make the step practically irreversible. If rate-limiting E_r is inhibited, then, the result will be just like that considered above. Similarly, if E_q, the step preceding the irreversible reaction, is rate-limiting and we inhibit E_q, B accumulates; even if D accumulates, however, it can have no effect on E_r. In any case, C drops, somewhat decreasing the velocity through E_r but the effect may be small since C has been near saturating concentration, and a new steady state is reached. Finally, consider inhibition of E_p when it is rate-limiting and E_r is irreversible. D accumulates; B falls; C falls and the E_r step is thus slowed. Unlike the result of the comparable linear case, the accumulation of D is limited. That is, the cyclic system maintains automatic self-regulation with all types of inhibition even when there is an irreversible step and regardless of the relative positions of the irreversible and rate-limiting steps.

These intuitive results obtained for the foregoing very simple models are obviously capable of extension. Even as they stand, however, these considerations provide some guidance relating to inhibitor studies in complex systems and some background against which to consider some aspects of metabolic control. In particular, the interplay of these kinds of velocity homeostasis (at the expense of concentration) inherent in coupled reaction networks and the kinds of concentration homeostasis (at the expense of velocity) inherent in regulation according to the energy charge concept (Chap. 15), for example, deserves some attention. Moreover, the implication of highly sensitive control inherent in the cyclic systems is of substantial interest. With a cycle operating at suboptimal substrate levels, addition of a small amount of any intermediate has a catalytic effect and hence great potential for signal amplification.

For those who wish to pursue such topics in the direction of fewer restrictive assumptions and more mathematical rigor, the papers of Waley (4), Hearon (5), and V. Ličko (6–8) are recommended. Special attention is called to the work of Britton Chance and his associates in this field (9–11). In the formal analysis of complex metabolic control, this group has done extensive fundamental work, both by computer simulation and by observing real biological systems.

GENERAL REFERENCES

Reiner, J. M.: *The Organism as an Adaptive Control System*, Prentice-Hall, Englewood Cliffs, 1968.

Webb, J. L.: *Enzyme and Metabolic Inhibitors*, Vol. I, Academic, New York, 1963.

Bray, H. G., and K. White: *Kinetics and Thermodynamics in Biochemistry*, 2nd ed., Academic, New York, 1966.

Chance, B., *et al.*: *Control of Energy Metabolism*, Academic, New York, 1966.

SPECIFIC REFERENCES

1. Prigogine, I.: *Introduction to Thermodynamics of Irreversible Processes*, Interscience, New York, 1961.
2. Eyring, H., R. P. Boyce, and J. D. Spikes: in M. Florkin and H. S. Mason (eds.), *Comparative Biochemistry*, Academic, New York, 1960.
3. Hearon, J. Z.: *Bull. Math. Biophys.*, **12**: 57 (1950).

4. Waley, S. G.: *Biochem. J.*, **91**: 514 (1964).
5. Hearon, J. Z.: *Physiol. Rev.*, **32**: 499 (1952).
6. Ličko, V.: *Bull. Math. Biophys.*, **25**: 141 (1963).
7. Ličko, V.: *Bull. Math. Biophys.*, **28**: 379 (1966).
8. Ličko, V.: *Bull. Math. Biophys.*, **29**: 1 (1967).
9. Chance, B.: *Cold Spring Harbor Symp. Quant. Biol.*, **26**: 289 (1961).
10. Chance, B., D. Garfinkel, J. Higgins, and B. Hess: *J. Biol. Chem.*, **235**: 2426 (1960).
11. Chance, B., B. Schoener, and S. Elsaesser: *Proc. Natl. Acad. Sci. U.S.*, **52**: 337 (1964).

APPENDIX

Problem-solving is often the best way to develop a feeling for the tools and their applications. The student who slugs it out with the following puzzles, easy at the start, much harder toward the end, should find his engagement with kinetic material rewarding. As these are primarily "thought questions," the author has made the hard decision not to spoil the fun by providing pat answers.

1. Demonstrate the equivalence of the three straight-line formulations of the simple Henri equation.
2. a. From the data in the accompanying table, find V, K_m, and k_{+2} by each of the three methods. Compare the methods for their usefulness in this application.
   b. Evaluate the three formulations under the circumstance that a systematic error (in reagent blank, say) causes an error of 2×10^{-6} in measurements of v_0. How will the error affect the values obtained for the constants?
   c. Evaluate the three formulations under the circumstance that "substrate inhibition" occurs at high substrate concentrations and the velocity at 2×10^{-3} M is found to be only 2.60×10^{-5}, while that at 1.5×10^{-3} M is 2.50×10^{-5}. How are you most likely to detect this effect?

Table of Data for Problem 2

A (moles/liter)	v_0 (moles/liter/min)
1.0×10^{-4}	6.70×10^{-6}
2.0×10^{-4}	1.10×10^{-5}
4.0×10^{-4}	1.70×10^{-5}
6.0×10^{-4}	2.00×10^{-5}
1.0×10^{-3}	2.40×10^{-5}
1.5×10^{-3}	2.65×10^{-5}
2.0×10^{-3}	2.80×10^{-5}

Enzyme concentration in all cases: $1.0 \times 10^{-9}\ M$

3. Consider the kinetic behavior of the simplest possible case of misorientation of a substrate in the active site of an enzyme: Enzyme E catalyzes a one-substrate reaction in which normal substrate PQ must complex at enzymic site P' to permit transfer of group Q to enzymic site Q'. The spontaneous dissociation of Q from Q' then regenerates the free enzyme. Since P has affinity only for P', no misorientation occurs. With alternate substrate RQ, however, the situation is different. Although R has the same affinity for P' as does P, the R group also tends to complex with Q', with the result that RQ is sometimes bound to the enzyme in backward orientation and fails to be split. In all cases, substrate binding is reversible and only a single molecule of substrate can complex with one molecule of enzyme at one time.

    Show, either by derivation of appropriate equations or by correct reasoning in words, what the kinetic effects of such misorientation would be. Explicitly, compare the nature of the double reciprocal plots of the E-catalyzed reactions of PQ and RQ and the relative values of the empirical constants obtainable from those plots by extrapolation.

4. An enzymologist is studying a reaction in which one of the substrates A^{2+} is a polyvalent cation over the pH range in which the enzyme is active. The enzymologist is worried about reversible "ion pairing" effects, as ion pairs of A^{2+} are probably not active as substrate. What would be the kinetic consequences of such ion pairing in a one-substrate mechanism? How could it be distinguished from other causes of similar behavior, such as some types of inhibition of the enzyme?

5. A number of reactions are known to be catalyzed by ion-exchange resins, which consist of insoluble polymers substituted with acidic or basic groups. List the kinds of reactions you might expect to be

catalyzed by ion exchangers and explain the catalytic mechanisms involved. In what important features, if any, would this catalysis differ from enzymic catalysis?

6. Show how k_{+1} and k_{-1} may be obtained from the variation of K_m with modifier concentration in one-substrate mechanisms where the sole function of the modifier is to affect the rate of conversion of the enzyme-substrate complex into free enzyme and final products.

7. Enzyme E catalyzes the reaction

$$XG + B \rightleftharpoons BG + X$$

When E is incubated with XG and isotopically labeled X in the absence of B and BG, the isotopic label is incorporated into XG at a rate comparable to the velocity of the overall reaction (observed in a separate experiment where E, XG, and B are incubated together). Although E is highly specific for XG, the specificity requirement for B is broad.

Devise a kinetic approach which might allow the foregoing data to be used in drawing a firm conclusion regarding the mechanism of action of E. Indicate the experiments to be done and the allowable interpretations of the possible alternative results.

8. The following information was obtained from double reciprocal plots of the initial velocities of the enzyme-catalyzed reaction $A + B \rightleftharpoons C + D$, where the concentration of A was systematically varied at each of three different concentrations of B.

[B] (M)	Apparent V (arbitrary units)	Apparent K_m for A
10^{-3}	1.4	.0032
10^{-2}	7.0	.016
0.1	12.0	.027

What conclusions may be reached regarding the reaction mechanism?

9. The kinetic consequence of double-displacement-type mechanisms has been asserted to be parallel double reciprocal plots. Can you develop a qualitative argument to show the necessity of this form? Does your explanation indicate whether (and why) this form must be obtained in plots for both substrates? Both uncompetitive inhibition (sometimes presumed to be the result of combination of the inhibitor with (EA) but not with E or A separately) and

misorientation also give rise to reciprocal plots parallel to the "normal" case. How might these phenomena be viewed in relation to your explanation?

10. Some enzymologists prefer to plot kinetic data in the v_0/A vs. v_0 linear form. Cleland uses double reciprocal plots. Wong and Hanes state a preference for the A/v_0 vs. A form. Show the types of patterns expected in each of these forms for extensive kinetic data obtained in the following two-substrate systems:

  a. a mechanism involving ternary complex formation by way of an obligatory sequence of substrates

  b. a mechanism involving a substituted enzyme intermediate

11. In two-substrate enzyme mechanisms what would be the kinetic consequences of the absence of any kinetically significant enzyme-substrate complexes?

12. Consider the following three-substrate formal mechanisms and the possibilities for distinguishing among them by studies involving variation of one substrate with other substrates at saturation in the presence of single products.

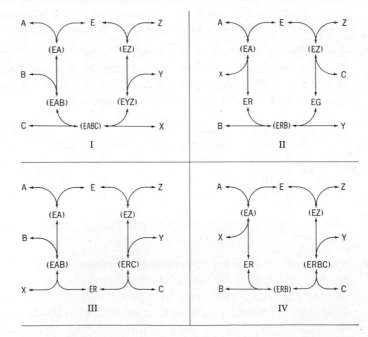

  a. Can mechanism I be distinguished from II by product inhibition studies using Y?

b. Can mechanism III be distinguished from IV using Z?

c. Can all four schemes be distinguished from each other by use of X and Y?

13. What can be concluded about the formal mechanisms of the following two reactions from the kinetic results given?

a. $BR + A \rightleftharpoons AR + B$. Subscript numbers indicate analogue substrates having the same transferable group.

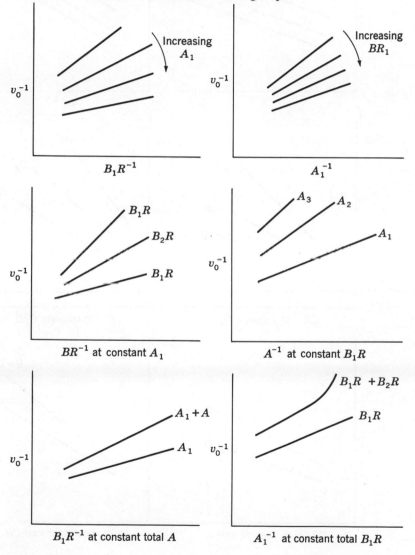

b. $CR + D \rightleftharpoons DR + C$. Subscript numbers indicate analogue substrates having the same transferable group.

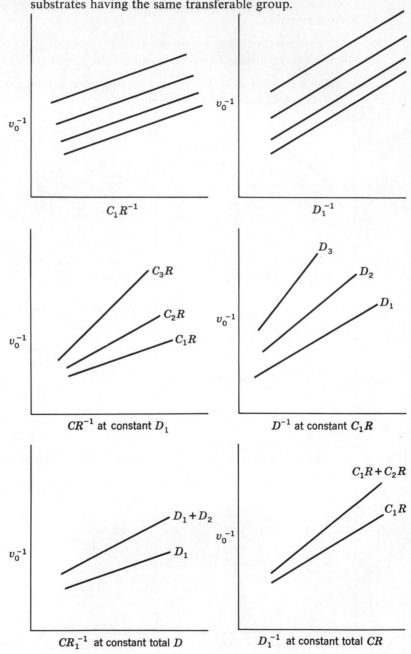

14. An amine oxidase is found to exhibit the kinetic behavior shown below, where A_1 refers to the concentration of the amine substrate so designated:

Data for the variation of the kinetic coefficients with pH are obtained for A_1 as the variable substrate and extrapolated to infinite O_2 concentration. The data are plotted in this form:

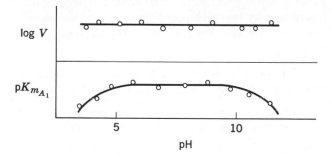

A second amine substrate A_2 yields data very like those for A_1 under the same conditions except that V for A_2 is substantially higher.

When the kinetic behavior of the system is studied as a function of ionic strength, with A_1 as the variable substrate and oxygen maintained at saturating levels, V is invariant, while the plot of $\log K_m^A$ vs. $\mu^{1/2}$ at low ionic strengths is a straight line of slope $+0.9$. When the dielectric constant is varied, at low ionic strength and substrate conditions as in the previous experiment, again V is invariant and a plot of $\log K_m^A$ vs. D^{-1} yields a straight line from which the electrostatic contribution to the entropy term is calculated as -8 e.u. A study of the effects of varying the temperature yields an overall entropy term of -1 e.u.

What can properly be concluded about the enzyme-catalyzed oxidation of A_1?

15. A highly purified enzyme catalyzes the hydrolysis of the phosphoric ester MP to MOH and inorganic phosphate. The double reciprocal

plots of data from kinetic experiments in which the concentration of MP is varied are straight lines. When the reaction is carried out in ^{18}O-labeled water, the inorganic phosphate obtained as product contains ^{18}O. Moreover, the enzyme catalyzes the rapid incorporation of ^{18}O from labeled inorganic phosphate into water in the absence of MP or MOH. Plots of the logarithm of initial velocity at very low MP concentration vs. pH are flat from pH 3 to pH 8.2, where they inflect downward, as they do again at pH 10. At pH values below 8.2, addition of methanol to reaction mixtures results in substantially increased velocity at low MP concentration. Methanol does not serve as a substrate. In the same range of pH and substrate concentration, the addition of ammonium sulfate causes decreased velocity. Both the methanol and salt effects diminish greatly at higher pH values. The enzyme is rapidly inactivated by the presence of low concentrations of diazonium salts, paramercuribenzoates, or dialkylphosphofluoridates (nerve gas).

Formulate as complete a tentative mechanism of action for this enzyme as is possible on the basis of the foregoing information.

16. It is announced in *The New York Times* that the renowned reaction $A + B \rightleftharpoons X + Y$ has been found to be catalyzed by the famous enzyme E. Kinetic data obtained in the E-catalyzed reaction show that the double reciprocal plots for A are straight lines that converge to the left of the ordinate at low concentrations of B but curves concave from above at high concentrations of B. On the other hand, the double reciprocal plots for B are converging straight lines at high concentrations of A but curves concave from above at low concentrations of A. The drudge who observed these facts cannot make head or tail of the thing, but six eminent theoretical enzymologists instantly issue statements citing these observations as conclusively demonstrating the catalytic mechanism. Unfortunately, however, each proposes a different mechanism. As a representative of a United Nations peace-keeping mission, class enzymes, subclass $A : B$ group transferases (E.C. 2.8.4.1), you are to establish which mechanism is correct. Are any of the following proposals in either category consistent with the data? Are they all? What additional experimental information might help clarify the situation?

The proposals are:

A. Essentially double-displacement mechanisms

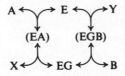

with any *one* of the following additions:

1. a regulatory (allosteric) site for A
2. the concomitant presence of an A-ase
3. competition by B for the A site *and* the presence of an extraneous competitor for B

B. Essentially single-displacement mechanisms

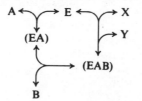

with any *one* of the following modifications:

1. no ternary complex is formed *and* B competes at the A site
2. *almost* random order, nonequilibrium, ternary complex (Only at low A does combination with B cause significant exclusion of A.)
3. random order, ternary complex but (over most of the range) equilibrium between E and substrates

INDEX

69 70 71　7 6 5 4 3 2 1